my revision notes

C000255347

AQA GCSE (9-1)

DESIGN AND TECHNOLOGY: TEXTILE-BASED MATERIALS

Ian Fawcett

Debbie Tranter

Pauline Treuherz

HODDER
EDUCATION

AN HACHETTE UK COMPANY

The Publishers would like to thank the following for permission to reproduce copyright material: p.1 © Stephan Goerlich/ imageBROKER / Alamy Stock Photo; p.3 © Stephen VanHorn/Shutterstock.com; p.4 © sportpoint/stock.adobe.com; p.08© Alonso Aguilar Als/123RF p.11 m © Evgenii Zadiraka/123 RF, p.11 b © Will Thomass/Shutterstock.com; p.30 t © Drillinginthedark/123RF, p.30 b © Angela Hampton Picture Library/Alamy Stock Photo; p.34 © 8th/stock.adobe.com; p.36 l © PzAxe/stock.adobe.com, p.36 r © Luisa Leal/stock.adobe.com; p.37 © Nataliia Pyzhova/stock.adobe.com; p.39 t © Orensila/stock.adobe.com, p.39 m © Apelöga/Astrakan Images/Alamy Stock Photo, p.39 b © Eduardo Lopez Coronado/123RF; p.40 © Maria Kraynova/123 RF; p.43 © Taviphoto/Shutterstock. com; p44 © Vjom/Shutterstock.com; p.49 © Forest Stewardship Council® - FSC® - www.fsc.org; p.49 © Fairtrade Foundation (http://www.fairtrade.org.uk/); p.51 © Hendrik Ballhausen/ dpa picture alliance archive / Alamy Stock Photo; p.101 © Michael DeFreitas / robertharding / Alamy Stock Photo; p.52 © Science & Society Picture Library/SSPL/Getty Images; p.55 © leonart /12RF; p.58 © Juliane Berger/Ingram Publishing/Alamy Stock Vector; p.63 Holger Burmeister/Alamy Stock Photo; p.64 © sebastien bonaime / Alamy Stock Photo; p.65 © Nomad_Soul/stock.adobe.com; p.67 © Incomible/Shutterstock.com; p.68 © Amelia Fox/stock.adobe.com; p.69 © Sveta3/stock.adobe.com; p.72 © wonderlandstock / Alamy Stock Photo; p.75 © Photobalance/stock.adobe.com

The authors and publishers would also like to thank the following schools and students for the examples of their student work: Abingdon School in Abingdon; Ripley St Thomas CE Academy in Lancaster; West Island School in Hong Kong; Oasis Academy, St Joseph's; Bedford Modern School in Bedford; Highgate School in London; Nonsuch High School for Girls in Surrey and Cameron Farquar at St George's School, Harpenden.

Every effort has been made to trace all copyright holders, but if any have been inadvertently overlooked, the Publishers will be pleased to make the necessary arrangements at the first opportunity.

Although every effort has been made to ensure that website addresses are correct at time of going to press, Hodder Education cannot be held responsible for the content of any website mentioned in this book. It is sometimes possible to find a relocated web page by typing in the address of the home page for a website in the URL window of your browser.

Hachette UK's policy is to use papers that are natural, renewable and recyclable products and made from wood grown in sustainable forests. The logging and manufacturing processes are expected to conform to the environmental regulations of the country of origin.

Orders:
please contact Bookpoint Ltd, 130 Park Drive, Milton Park, Abingdon, Oxon OX14 4SE.
Telephone: (44) 01235 827720.
Fax: (44) 01235 400401.
Email education@bookpoint.co.uk
Lines are open from 9 a.m. to 5 p.m., Monday to Saturday, with a 24-hour message answering service. You can also order through our website: www.hoddereducation.co.uk

© Ian Fawcett, Debbie Tranter and Pauline Treuherz, 2018

ISBN 978-1-5104-3230-7

First published in 2018 by
Hodder Education,
An Hachette UK Company
Carmelite House
50 Victoria Embankment
London EC4Y 0DZ
www.hoddereducation.co.uk
Impression number   10   9   8   7   6   5   4   3   2   1
Year   2022   2021   2020   2019   2018

Cover photo © Natika – stock.adobe.com

Typeset in India.

Printed in Spain.

A catalogue record for this title is available from the British Library.

Get the most from this book

Everyone has to decide their own revision strategy, but it is essential to review your work, learn key facts and test your understanding. These Revision Notes will help you to do that in a planned way, topic by topic. You can check your progress by ticking off each section as you revise.

Tick to track your progress

Use the revision planner on pages iv to viii to plan your revision, topic by topic. Tick each box when you have:

- revised and understood a topic
- tested yourself
- practised the exam questions and gone online to check your answers and complete the quick quizzes.

You can also keep track of your revision by ticking off each topic heading in the book. You may find it helpful to add your own notes as you work through each topic.

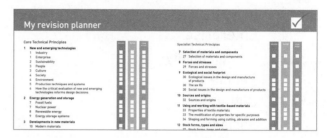

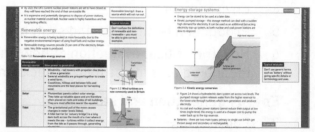

Features to help you succeed

Exam tips

Expert tips are given throughout the book to help you polish your exam technique in order to maximise your chances in the exam.

Typical mistakes

The authors identify the typical mistakes candidates make and explain how you can avoid them.

Now test yourself

These short, knowledge-based questions provide the first step in testing your learning. Answers are at the back of the book.

Key words

Key words from the specification are highlighted in bold throughout the book.

Exam practice

Practice exam questions are provided at the end of each section. Use them to consolidate your revision and practise your exam skills.

Online

Go online to check your answers to the exam questions and try out the extra quick quizzes at **www.hoddereducation.co.uk/myrevisionnotes**

My revision planner

Core Technical Principles

REVISED   TESTED   EXAM READY

Exam practice answers at **www.hoddereducation.co.uk/6 myrevisionnotesdownloads**

Designing and Making Principles

REVISED   TESTED   EXAM READY

Now test yourself answers, exam practice answers
and quick quizzes at www.hoddereducation.co.uk/myrevisionnotes

1 New and emerging technologies

New technologies change the way we live. They can have an impact on how we communicate, live and work, and how we manufacture and use products.

Industry

- Before the Industrial Revolution, most people worked in farming communities, in small workshops or at home. The development of steam-powered technology meant products could be produced faster and more cheaply in factories. Many people moved to towns and cities to work in these factories.
- Modern factories are usually large warehouses located near transport links that contain manufacturing machinery used for **assembly-line production**.
- Developments in computers and processors that can control machines (**computer numerically controlled** or CNC machines) have led to increasing **automation** of repetitive tasks.
- **Robotics** are now used extensively in many industries. Robot arms can perform many tasks on a production line with precision and speed, replacing human operators.

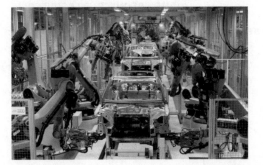

Figure 1.1 Robot arms are now used in many industries, including the car industry

- Developments in communication technology have also changed where and how we work.
- The internet and mobile technology (particularly broadband and wifi) mean we can now communicate quickly and easily with people at anytime and anywhere. We can work remotely, and with people based in different places all around the world.

> **Assembly-line production**: a series of workers and machines in a factory who progressively assemble identical items.
>
> **Computer numerically controlled (CNC)**: automated machines which are operated by computers.
>
> **Automation**: the use of automatic equipment in manufacturing.
>
> **Robotics**: technology involved in the design, building, operation and use of robots.
>
> **Innovation**: inventing and developing ideas into products.

Enterprise

- Businesses and entrepreneurs look for gaps in the market and aim to develop creative new ideas, invent new products and bring them to market.
- **Innovation** is often made possible by new and emerging technologies. These technologies can allow existing products or processes to be improved, or products and processes be developed in a completely new way.

- **Crowdfunding** is a method of raising money for a project by getting lots of people to give small amounts of money. It has been made possible by the development of the internet and social media.
- Many retailers now sell their products online. This is called **virtual retailing**.
- Retailers also make use of **virtual marketing**. This uses websites, social media and email to market a product and increase brand awareness.
- Tech **co-operatives** have also been made possible by new technologies. These are worker-owned businesses that provide technical support and consulting to other companies with communications and computer technology goods and services.
- Social media and the internet have allowed people to connect directly with producers of products and have increased awareness of fair trade. The **fair trade** movement aims to achieve fair and improved trading conditions for producers in developing countries and to promote sustainability.

Sustainability

REVISED

- Product manufacture uses a huge number of resources. Processing raw materials and converting them into products consumes huge amounts of energy.
- **Sustainability** is about meeting our own present-day needs without compromising the needs of future generations. New technologies can be used to help us manufacture products more sustainably.
- **Finite resources** are those that do not renew themselves quickly. Their use is not sustainable and therefore should be limited.
- **Non-finite resources** can be replenished quickly and are therefore more sustainable than finite resources.

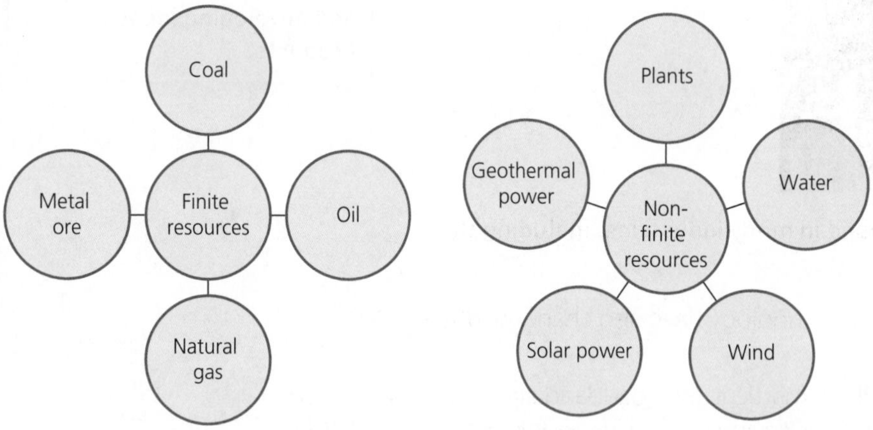

Crowdfunding: a method of funding a project by raising money from large numbers of people using the internet.

Virtual marketing: marketing techniques that get websites, social networks or their users to pass on marketing messages to other websites and users to increase brand awareness.

Virtual retailing: selling products on the internet.

Co-operative: a business owned, governed and self-managed by its workers.

Fair trade: a movement that aims to achieve fair and better trading conditions and opportunities that promote sustainability for developing countries.

Sustainability: designing to maintain the environment today and in the future.

Finite resource: a resource that will run out.

Non-finite resource: a resource that if managed properly will not run out.

Figure 1.2 New technologies have helped us to make use of more sustainable non-finite resources

- At the end of a product's life its disposal can have an impact on the environment. Landfill can cause pollution, damage animal habitats and create noise and destruction. New technologies are helping to develop alternatives to landfill and developments in materials and recycling technology mean more products can now be recycled at the end of their life.

People

- Designers create new products because of customer need or because of developments in technology.
- **Technology push** is where new technologies or materials are developed, leading to designers developing new products that use them. The Apple iPad is an example of technology push (people didn't know they wanted it until it was launched).
- **Market pull** is where users want an existing product to be improved or redeveloped to meet their needs. Market research is carried out to identify how existing products can be improved to meet those needs. For example, BMW redeveloped the iconic Mini car of the 1950s to meet the needs of modern car users.
- Developments in technology have caused some jobs to disappear. Automation and robotics on production lines have replaced factory workers in some cases (although new jobs have been created in designing, manufacturing, programming and maintaining machinery).
- Some traditional job roles still exist, but new technologies have changed the way tasks are performed. For example, designers now often use CAD (computer aided design) software rather than hand-drawn designs; people use computers and email to communicate rather than typewriters and letters.

> **Technology push:** where new technologies or materials are developed and designers develop new products that use them.
>
> **Market pull:** where users want an existing product to be improved or redeveloped to meet their needs.
>
> **Culture:** the values, beliefs, customs and behaviours of groups of people and societies.

Culture

- **Culture** means the values, beliefs, customs and behaviours of groups of people and societies.
- Fashions and trends often influence the design of products. These can be influenced by different groups of people (for example, musicians, film stars or celebrities) and are often driven by the challenge to keep up with the latest technology.
- It is important for designers to understand and respect the views and beliefs of different cultures, including those of different faiths and with different religious beliefs, when designing products.

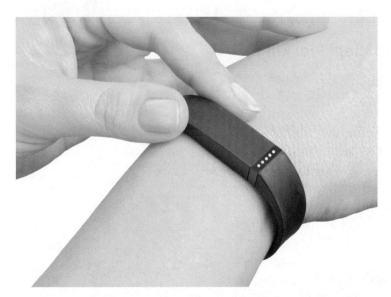

Figure 1.3 Fashions and trends can be driven by a desire to keep up with the latest technology

Society

- Designers have a responsibility to design products that meet the needs of everyone in society. They must take into account that different groups (for example, disabled or elderly people, or different religious groups) have different needs.

- Developments in technology have led to the emergence of products that help those with a disability to carry out everyday activities. For example, 3D printing and bio-electronics are helping to produce prosthetics to replace missing limbs and give disabled people extra functionality.

- New technologies have also allowed designers to consider the needs of the elderly. Products include: smartphones designed specifically for the elderly with simplified interfaces, larger buttons and screens, detachable keypads, hearing aid compatibility and louder speakers.

- Different faiths may interpret colours, symbols, shapes and ideas differently, and an awareness of these can contribute to the success of a product.

Figure 1.4 Developments in technology have helped those with a disability to carry out a range of activities

Environment

Continuous improvement and efficient working

- Designers can use new technologies to continually improve their products and working practices, making them more efficient and improving their performance.

- Continuous improvement can save time and make use of fewer resources, reducing costs and environmental impact.

- The increased efficiency of products can be positive for the environment. For example, if an electrically-powered product is made more efficient, it will use less energy and therefore put less pressure on non-finite resources. Using less material in a product can have a similarly positive impact.

- Efficient working processes can also be beneficial for the environment. Efficient, automated production lines can produce products very quickly. Computer-controlled machines and robots are very precise, leading to fewer errors and less waste.

Pollution and global warming

- Producing new products uses up valuable resources such as oil, metal ores and timber.
- Converting raw materials into products uses energy, which if produced by burning fossil fuels releases pollutants including smoke, sulphur dioxide, carbon monoxide and carbon dioxide (CO_2).
- CO_2 is a greenhouse gas that contributes to **global warming**.
- Technology that uses alternative energy sources such as the sea, wind, sun and rivers can help to minimise the impact of products on the environment.

Production techniques and systems

- Most production lines are now automated and make use of CNC machines that allow products to be made quickly and accurately.
- **Computer-aided design (CAD)** allows designers to design and model on screen. Designs can be manipulated and adapted easily and shared from anywhere in the world.
- **Computer-aided manufacture (CAM)** allows CAD designs to be produced. It is faster and more efficient than traditional manufacturing methods. Using CAM also increases precision as well as efficiency and speed.
- **Flexible manufacturing systems (FMS)** organise production into cells of CNC machines, with each cell performing a different task. FMS are very flexible – they can be set up to produce new products quickly and easily.
- **Just in time (JIT) production** is a production method that means materials arrive at a factory just in time for production.
- JIT allows for **lean manufacturing**, which focuses on reducing waste.

Global warming: an increase in the temperature of the Earth's atmosphere due to higher levels of CO_2.

Computer-aided design (CAD): design work created on computer software packages which can control CAM machines.

Computer-aided manufacture (CAM): machines which manufacture products, controlled by computers.

Flexible manufacturing system (FMS): flexibility in a system which allows it to react to predicted or unpredicted changes during manufacturing.

Just in time (JIT) production: reduces flow time within production as items needed are delivered just in time for the assembly of the product.

Lean manufacturing: focusing on reduction of waste when manufacturing.

How the critical evaluation of new and emerging technologies informs design decisions

- Planned obsolescence – this is when a manufacturer designs a product to have a shorter lifespan.
- Products become **obsolete** or unfashionable or just stop functioning as efficiently – this allows manufacturers to bring out a new version of the product and keep sales at a steady level.
- This creates waste as products are thrown away and so impacts on the environment.
- Design for maintenance – performing functions on a product to help keep it working correctly throughout its life.
- Some products are made up of modules which can be repaired and replaced, rather than the whole product having to be replaced. Modules also allow for parts of the product (like a PC) to be upgraded.
- **Ethics** – to keep prices low, companies cut costs in a variety of ways.
- Automated factories lower workforce costs, but people are forced out of their jobs.
- Using countries with cheap labour reduces costs, but working conditions are invariably poor.
- The environment – manufacturing a product uses **raw materials** and energy which impact on the environment.
- Designers need to consider how the product will be used, what materials will be used and the disposal of the product.
- End of life disposal – if a product can be recycled after use, then there is less impact on the environment as less of the raw materials are needed to make new products.
- Plastics can be sorted after they have been used using their recycle number.
- Aluminium can be re-melted into **ingots** and used in other products.
- Glass bottles are usually re-used. They can be sterilised and re-filled, which requires very little processing.
- Glass however does not degrade so can be recycled over and over again.
- If a product does have to go into landfill at the end of its useful life, it should be made from **biodegradable** materials.
- Non-biodegradable materials take hundreds of years to break down.

Obsolete: something which is no longer useful, or out of date.

Ethics: moral principles.

Raw materials: before they have undergone processing, the state a material is first found in (for example, ores from the ground before they are processed into metals).

Ingots: bars of metal that can be processed.

Biodegradable: something which breaks down and degrades naturally.

Exam tip

Make sure that you understand key terminology and can give a definition. This will help you when you attempt multiple choice-style questions.

Typical mistake

If a question asks for a description, comparison or analysis, you will lose marks if your answer lacks depth.

Now test yourself

1 Explain the benefits of using automation in a factory. [4 marks]
2 Explain the term 'virtual retailing'. [2 marks]
3 Give an example of where technology push has produced a new product. [2 marks]
4 Why do designers need to consider the needs of everyone in society when designing a product? [4 marks]
5 Explain the term JIT production. [2 marks]

2 Energy generation and storage

Electricity is our main power supply and we are very dependent upon it. You need to understand how it is supplied and stored, and what alternative fuels are available.

Fossil fuels

- Britain relies on **fossil fuels** to provide energy.
- All fuels have to be burnt to produce heat. In electricity generation, heat is used to convert water to steam, which then drives **turbines** connected to **generators**.
- Burning fuel creates CO_2 which adds to the **greenhouse effect**.
- Power stations can be built anywhere to convert fossil fuels into electricity, but they need a water supply.

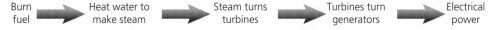

Burn fuel → Heat water to make steam → Steam turns turbines → Turbines turn generators → Electrical power

Figure 2.1 Energy conversion

- Coal – 23 per cent of UK electricity comes from coal-fired power stations, so coal is imported from abroad as deep-pit mining has stopped in Britain.
  - Mining and burning coal releases pollutants into the atmosphere, such as sulphur dioxide.
  - Waste tips, stock piles and open pits look unsightly and are hazardous.
  - The advantage of using coal is that it needs no processing before burning.
- Natural gas – this is Britain's main source of power for electricity production.
  - It is used for heating and cooking and can be used directly without the need for processing. It is transported through pipelines.
  - Methane is the main natural gas and is found deep underground.
  - The majority of Britain's supply comes from pipelines connected to Europe.
- Oil – this is hardly used to produce electricity in Britain.
  - It needs to be processed and refined from crude oil.
  - Stocks of oil will run out before coal.
- Although there are deposits of shale gas under Britain, it is thought that accessing these could pollute our water supplies and cause earthquakes.

> **Fossil fuels**: coal, oil and gas, which are finite resources and are found naturally.
>
> **Greenhouse effect**: pollution in the atmosphere causes the sun's heat to get trapped in the lower atmosphere and warm up the planet.
>
> **Fission**: division or splitting of an atom.
>
> **Turbines**: a wheel inside a machine is rotated by a flow of water, or other fluid, or steam or gas.
>
> **Generators**: machines for converting mechanical energy into electricity.

Nuclear power

- **Fission** is the splitting of uranium atoms to produce heat – this occurs in nuclear reactors.
- Huge amounts of energy can be produced in this way from a small quantity of uranium.
- The heat produced is used to heat water and convert it to steam, which is then used to power generators in the same way as with fossil fuels.

- By 2025 the UK's current nuclear power stations are set to have closed as they will have reached the end of their serviceable life.
- It is expensive and potentially dangerous to dispose of power stations, as nuclear material could leak. Nuclear waste is highly hazardous and has long-lasting effects.

Renewable energy

REVISED

- **Renewable** energy is being looked at more favourably due to the negative environmental impact of using fossil fuels and nuclear energy.
- Renewable energy sources provide 25 per cent of the electricity Britain uses. Very little waste is produced.

Table 1.2 Renewable energy sources

Renewable energy source	How power is generated
Wind	• Windmills – tall towers with propeller-like blades – drive a generator. • Several windmills are grouped together to create a wind farm. • Coastlines, hilltops and between hills and mountains are the best places for harvesting wind.
Solar	• Photovoltaic panels collect solar energy. • They take up valuable space and are therefore often placed on roofs and sides of tall buildings. • They are most effective nearer the equator.
Tidal	• The gravitational pull of the moon causes changes in water levels (tides). • A tidal barrier (or 'estuary bridge') is a long dam built across the mouth of a river where it meets the sea – turbines within it collect energy from the tide as it passes through, generating electricity. • A disadvantage is that rivers never empty and mudflats can flood, ruining birds' habitats
Hydroelectricity	• A dam is used to block a river and create a water reserve. This is stored in a reservoir and channelled through turbines, which turn generators. • Electricity can be produced very quickly.
Wave	• Energy provided by the up and down movement of a wave is either converted into mechanical energy to move pistons or compress air to force it through a turbine. • This energy is difficult to collect.
Biomass	• Plants are grown to burn, or decaying plants and animal matter are used to produce heat. • Oilseed rape and willow are harvested as biomass crops and can be regrown quickly. • Some vegetable oils are treated after cooking to use for diesel engines. • Burning plants causes atmospheric pollution (but is less harmful than burning fossil fuels).

Renewable (energy): from a source which will not run out.

Typical mistake

Don't confuse the definitions of renewable and non-renewable – you must be able to give correct examples.

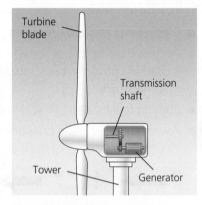

Figure 2.2 Wind turbines are now commonly used in Britain

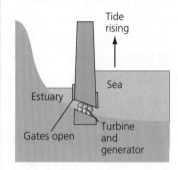

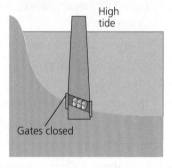

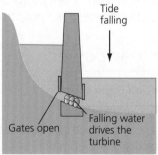

Figure 2.3 Tidal energy

Exam practice answers at **www.hoddereducation.co.uk/6 myrevisionnotesdownloads**

Energy storage systems

- Energy can be stored to be used at a later date.
- Kinetic pumped storage – this storage method can deal with a sudden high demand for electricity. It can be used as an additional fast-acting electricity top-up system, as both nuclear and coal power stations are slow to respond.

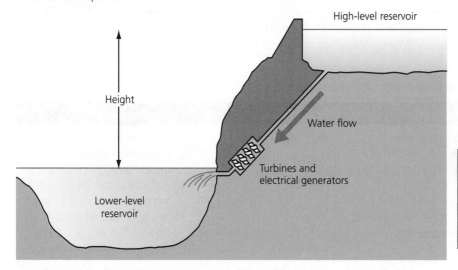

High-level reservoir

Height

Water flow

Turbines and electrical generators

Lower-level reservoir

Figure 2.4 Kinetic energy conversion

> **Typical mistake**
>
> Don't use generic terms such as 'battery' without giving specific details or terminology and uses.

- Figure 2.4 shows a hydroelectric dam system set across two levels. The pumped storage system releases water from the higher reservoir to the lower one through turbines which turn generators and produce electricity.
- As coal and nuclear power stations cannot reduce their output at low times (night-time), this energy is used at a cheaper cost to pump the water back up to the top reservoir.
- Batteries – there are two main types: primary or single use (which get thrown away) and secondary or rechargeable.
  - Batteries provide electrical energy away from a mains supply, so are useful in portable products.
  - Primary batteries are alkaline and zinc-carbon and typically produce about 1.5 volts per cell.
  - Rechargeable batteries are more expensive to buy than single-use batteries, but are cost-efficient in the long run as they don't need to be replaced, only recharged.

> **Exam tip**
>
> Understand the advantages and disadvantages of each type of energy and storage to score higher marks, so that you are able to draw comparisons and make conclusions.

Now test yourself

1. Explain a way of producing electricity in a series of stages. [5 marks]
2. Discuss the problems associated with the use of biomass as a renewable energy source. [2 marks]
3. List three ways to store energy, and describe one in detail. [3 marks]

3 Developments in new materials

Modern materials

Modern materials are materials that have been produced through the invention or discovery of new processes. A designer will make use of these to make new and improved products.

Table 3.1 Modern materials, their properties and applications

Modern material	Description	Properties	Applications
Graphene	Graphene is a two-dimensional layer of carbon. It is harder than diamond, 300 times stronger than steel and is currently the lightest known material.	Very lightweight Transparent Flexible Tough Very good conductor of electricity	The use of graphene is in development but potential applications include solar-powered smartphones that charge in seconds and water filters that will produce clean water for everyone.
Metal foam	Metal foam is produced by injecting gas into metal when it is in a molten state.	Very lightweight High compressive strength Porous Excellent energy-absorbing properties	Soundproofing in cars As a crash protection safety feature
Titanium	Titanium is a relatively new metal.	High strength to density ratio Excellent resistance to corrosion	Surgical instruments and replacement body parts such as hip joints
Liquid crystal display (LCD)	An LCD is a laminate of two layers of glass with a liquid crystal core.	Opaque (when an electrical current is applied to the liquid crystal core)	Flat screen televisions
Nano materials	Nano materials are very, very small: one-billionth of a metre in size. They are added to other materials to improve their properties.	Can be coated onto glass to make it 'self-cleaning' Can be added to sports equipment to make it lighter and stronger Antibacterial qualities	Glass, sports equipment, antibacterial socks
Polytetrafluorethylene (PTFE)	PTFE is a non-stick coating applied to surfaces to make then slippery.	Non-stick	Kitchen utensils and pans (these are often coated 'Teflon')
Corn starch polymers	Corn starch polymers are made from polylactic acid that is found in potatoes, corn and maze. It is an alternative to oil-based polymers.	Renewable Biodegradable	Disposable cutlery and food packaging

Modern material	Description	Properties	Applications
Anodised aluminium	A coating applied to aluminium by an electrolytic process.	Hardens the surface of aluminium. It can have a dye applied to change the appearance of the aluminium.	Sports drinks bottles, components for climbing equipment and mountain bikes
Nickel plating	A coating applied to metal by an electrolytic process.	Prevents corrosion and wear of the base metal	Door handles, belt buckles, nuts and bolts
Polymer-coated steel	A coating of a thermoforming polymer applied to hot metal.	Prevents corrosion and alters the appearance of the base metal	Tool handles

Figure 3.1 Anodised carabiners

Smart materials

A **smart material** can have its properties altered by a change in external stimuli. This can be by heat, light, stress, moisture or pH.

● **Shape memory alloys (SMAs)** will return to their original shape when heated.
● **Thermochromatic** pigments change colour at varying temperatures.

Figure 3.2 These babies' feeding spoons change colour when heated

● **Photochromic** pigments change colour depending on how much light is present.

Modern material: a material that has recently been developed.

Smart material: a material that reacts to environmental changes such as heat and light.

Shape memory alloy (SMA): a metal that will return to its original shape when placed in hot water.

Thermochromatic: a material that reacts to heat.

Photochromic: a material that reacts to light.

Typical mistake

It is easy to confuse the terms 'modern material' and 'smart material' under the pressure of the exam. Make sure you know the difference to prevent losing marks.

Composite materials

A **composite material** is made up of two or more materials, and is designed to enhance the properties of the material.

- Glass-reinforced polymer (GRP) is made from strands of glass mixed with a polyester resin. This produces a strong, mouldable material that is tough and waterproof. It is commonly used to manufacture canoes, boat hulls and 'kit cars'.
- Carbon-fibre reinforced plastic (CFRP) is very similar to GRP but uses carbon fibre instead of stands of glass. This makes it lightweight and very strong. It is used in the production of Formula One racing cars and expensive bicycles.

Technical textiles

Technical textiles are manufactured for their functional capabilities rather than their aesthetic appearance.

- **Conductive fabrics** have conductive fibres or conductive powders impregnated into them. They allow electrical currents to be passed through them. Fencing suits use '**e-textiles**' to record a score.
- Fire-resistant fabrics use meta-aramid to increase their resistance to fire. A firefighter's suit uses this material to help protect the user from flames while still being flexible and breathable.
- Kevlar is a combination of terephthaloyl chloride and para-phenylenediamine mixed with a layer of resin. This produces a very light, very strong material that can withstand extremes of temperature. This makes it an ideal material for the manufacture of bulletproof vests and safety clothing.
- Microfibres are very fine synthetic fibres that are used for outdoor clothing and sportswear. They are breathable, durable, crease-resistant and easy to care for.

> **Exam tip**
>
> Make sure that you know the name of at least one modern material, one smart material, one composite material and one technical textile. Be ready to give uses for that material and explain its properties.

Composite material: a material that combines the properties of two or more materials.

Technical textiles: textiles manufactured for their functional capabilities.

Conductive fabrics: textiles that conduct electricity.

E-textiles: textiles that use smart materials.

Now test yourself

1 Give the name of a suitable protective coating for aluminium. [1 mark]
2 Explain the advantages of using corn starch polymers for food packaging. [4 marks]
3 What is meant by the term 'smart material'? [2 marks]
4 Explain why carbon fibre reinforced plastic is used to manufacture the body of a Formula One racing car. [4 marks]
5 Give the name of a technical textile and suggest a suitable use. [2 marks]

4 Systems approach to designing

- Electronic systems are used to provide functionality to products and processes.
- A **system** is a set of parts that work together.
- Electronic systems have three different elements: input, process and output.
- A systems diagram is used to show how an operation breaks down into these three elements and to describe what is happening in a system.

Figure 4.1 This systems diagram shows the input, process and output for a street light sensor

Inputs

REVISED

- **Input devices** are electrical and/or mechanical sensors.
- They use signals from the environment (for example, heat, light or pressure) and convert them into signals that can be passed to processing devices and components.
- A **light-dependent resistor (LDR)** is an input device used to detect light levels.
- When levels of light are low, resistance is high and low levels of electrical current flow through it; in intense light, it has low resistance and the level of current flowing increases.
- LDRs are used in street lights, night lights and clock radios.
- A temperature sensor or **thermistor** is a component in which resistance changes with changes in temperature.
- In some thermistors, resistance increases when temperature increases; in others, resistance falls when temperature increases.
- Thermistors are used in toasters, refrigerators and hairdryers.
- Pressure sensors – resistance changes with changes in pressure.
- **Switches** are useful input devices that sense when pressure is applied. Different types are used in many different products.

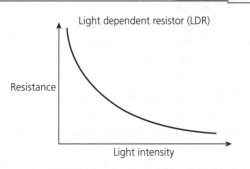

Figure 4.2 An LDR's resistance decreases as light intensity increases

> **System**: a set of parts or components that work together and provide functionality to products and processes.
>
> **Input device**: an electrical or mechanical sensor that uses signals from the environment and converts them into signals that can be passed to processing devices and components.
>
> **Light-dependent resistor (LDR)**: an input device used to detect light levels in which resistance increases in low light and decreases in intense light.
>
> **Thermistor**: an input device in which resistance changes with changes in temperature.
>
> **Switch**: an input device that senses when pressure is applied.

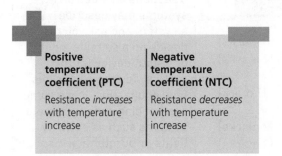

Positive temperature coefficient (PTC)	Negative temperature coefficient (NTC)
Resistance *increases* with temperature increase	Resistance *decreases* with temperature increase

Figure 4.3 Thermistors either increase or decrease resistance when they detect increases in temperature

Processes

- **Process devices** handle information received from an input device and turn outputs on and/or off.
- In electronic systems, processes are often controlled by an **integrated circuit (IC)**.
- A **microcontroller** is the most frequently used IC; it is a small computer within a single IC used to provide functionality to a product.
- Microcontrollers can be used as counters, timers and for decision-making in electronic systems.
- Designers often use flowcharts with standard symbols to describe the operation of a program.

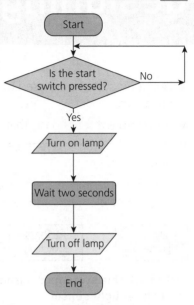

Figure 4.4 This flowchart describes a program that flashes an LED on and off

Outputs

- **Output devices** send out information (such as, heat, light, sound or movement) to the environment.
- Lamps pass electric current through a thin tungsten filament that operates in a glass bulb. They produce a lot of light and heat but have poor energy efficiency and have been replaced by LEDs in many products.
- Buzzers and speakers are sound output devices often used in alarm devices and timers. They can also confirm user input such as a button press or a mouse click.
- **Light-emitting diodes (LEDs)** are usually round and 5 mm in diameter (although they are available in a range of shapes, sizes and colours). They are very bright and often used as indicators on control panels.

Process device: a device that handles information received from an input device and turn outputs on and/or off.

Integrated circuit (IC): a self-contained circuit made up of separate components that act as process devices in an electronic system.

Microcontroller: a small computer with a single integrated circuit used to provide functionality and control.

Output device: a device that sends out information to the environment.

Light-emitting diode (LED): an output device that produces light.

Typical mistake

Try not to confuse the functions of microcontrollers and microprocessors. *Microcontrollers* are used in integrated circuits to run a set sequence of instructions. *Microprocessors* used in computers carry out many different tasks.

Exam tip

Questions on electronic systems may describe a system and ask you to decide on a suitable input or output device for the system. To prepare for this type of question, learn some system diagrams for simple systems such as security lights or burglar alarms.

Now test yourself

TESTED

1 Name three input devices. [3 marks]
2 Explain how an LDR works. [2 marks]
3 State what the input device would be in a system designed to alert a person to an intruder in their home. [1 mark]
4 Describe how a microcontroller is used in an electronic system. [2 marks]
5 Name three output devices. [3 marks]

5 Mechanical devices

A **mechanism** is a device that changes an input motion into an output motion.

Different types of movement

There are four different types of movement:

- **Linear** motion – movement in a straight line: for example, a conveyor belt
- **Rotary** motion – movement round in a circle: for example, a wheel
- **Reciprocating** motion – movement backwards and forwards in a straight line: for example, a needle in a sewing machine
- **Oscillating** motion – movement swinging from side to side: for example, a pendulum in a clock.

Changing magnitude and direction of force

Mechanisms can change the amount of movement and the direction of movement.

Levers

- A **lever** is a simple mechanism that changes an *input* motion and force into an *output* motion and force.
- The input force is called the **effort**. This is the force applied to move the object.
- The output is called the **load**. This is the object to be moved.
- A lever moves around a fixed point called a **pivot** or **fulcrum**.

There are three types or orders of lever:

- A **first-order lever** has the fulcrum anywhere between the effort and the load. The closer the fulcrum is to the load, the less effort needed to move it.

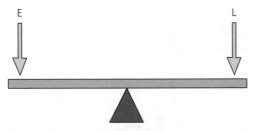

Figure 5.1 A seesaw is an example of a first-order lever

- A **second-order lever** has the load and effort on the same side of the fulcrum. Because the load is nearer the fulcrum, less effort is needed to move it. An example would be a wheelbarrow.

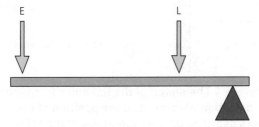

Figure 5.2 A second-order lever

> **Mechanism**: a device that changes an input motion into an output motion.
>
> **Linear motion**: movement in a straight line.
>
> **Rotary motion**: movement round in a circle.
>
> **Reciprocating motion**: movement backwards and forwards in a straight line.
>
> **Oscillating motion**: movement swinging from side to side.
>
> **Lever**: a simple mechanism that changes an input motion and force into an output motion and force.
>
> **Effort**: an input force applied to move an object.
>
> **Load**: an output force.
>
> **Pivot** or **fulcrum**: a fixed point around which a mechanism moves.
>
> **First-order lever**: a lever that has the fulcrum anywhere between the effort and the load.
>
> **Second-order lever**: a lever that has the load and effort on the same side of the fulcrum.

- A **third-order lever** has the load and effort on the same side of the fulcrum, but the load is further away from the fulcrum and therefore the effort needed is greater than the load. Barbeque tongs would be an example of a third-order lever.

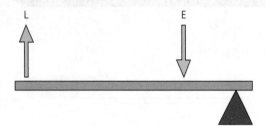

Figure 5.3 A third-order lever

Rotary systems

- Mechanisms that control and change rotary motion have a turning force that causes rotation, which is called **torque**.
- Rotary mechanisms can either reduce rotary speed and increase torque, or increase rotary speed and reduce torque.

Cams and followers

- A **cam and follower** converts rotary motion into reciprocating motion: when the cam rotates, the follower moves up and down.
- The pattern in which the follower moves up and down is controlled by the shape of the cam.
- The follower can rise (go up), fall (go down) or dwell (stay still).

Simple gear trains

- A **gear train** is a mechanism that transmits rotary motion and torque.
- A gear train has a driver gear (input) and a driven gear (output) – these are wheels that have teeth around the edge that interlock.
- Different sized gears connected together either increase or decrease the speed of rotation and increase or decrease the torque.
- The smaller gear will rotate faster than the larger gear.
- The gears will rotate in opposite directions.

Linkages

- A **linkage** is a mechanism that transfers force and changes the direction of movement.
- The number and shapes of the linkages can change the direction of the force.
- The position of the pivots can change the size or magnitude of the force.
- A **bell crank linkage** changes the direction of the input motion through 90°.
- It has one fixed pivot and two moving pivots.
- In a **push/pull** linkage (or **parallel motion** linkage), the direction of motion and the magnitude of the forces are the same.
- It has two fixed pivots and four moving pivots.

> **Third-order lever**: a lever that has the load and effort on the same side of the fulcrum, but the load is further away from the fulcrum and therefore the effort needed is greater than the load.
>
> **Torque**: a turning force that causes rotation.

> **Typical mistake**
>
> Don't be confused about the direction of movement in different rotary systems. Remember that in gear trains the gears move in the *opposite* direction, but belts and pulleys move in the *same* direction.

> **Cam and follower**: a mechanism that converts rotary motion into reciprocating motion when the cam rotates and the follower moves up and down.
>
> **Gear train**: a mechanism with two wheels with teeth around the edge that interlock and transmit rotary motion and torque.

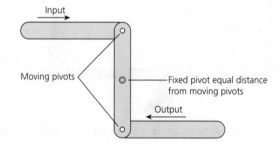

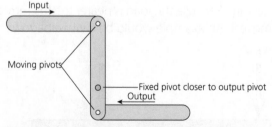

Figure 5.4 The shape of the linkage can change the direction of force, and the position of the pivots can change the magnitude of the force

Exam practice answers at **www.hoddereducation.co.uk/6 myrevisionnotesdownloads**

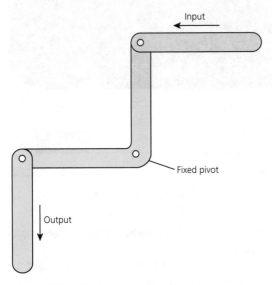

Figure 5.5 A bell crank linkage changes the direction of the input motion through 90°

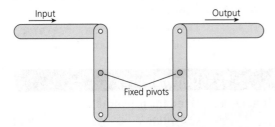

Figure 5.6 In a push/pull linkage the input and output motion are in the same direction

Pulleys and belts

- **Pulleys** (wheels with grooves in their rim) **and belts** (which connect two pulleys) transmit rotary motion to rotary motion.
- Different sized pulleys connected together either increase or decrease the speed of rotation and increase or decrease the torque transmitted.
- When the driver pulley is larger than the driven pulley, the driven pulley will spin faster but the torque will be less.
- When the driver pulley is smaller than the driven pulley, the driven pulley will spin slower but the torque will be increased.

> **Linkage**: a mechanism that transfers force and changes the direction of movement.
>
> **Bell crank linkage**: a linkage that changes the direction of the input motion through 90°.
>
> **Push/pull** or **parallel motion linkage**: a linkage in which the direction of motion and the magnitude of the forces are the same.
>
> **Pulleys and belts**: a mechanism of two small wheels connected by a belt that transmit rotary motion to rotary motion.

> **Exam tip**
>
> Questions are likely to test your knowledge of the functions of mechanical devices to produce different sorts of movement and to change the magnitude and direction of forces. Make sure you know the types of movement each different mechanical device produces, and – for linkages and rotary systems – how they change the size and direction of force.

Now test yourself

TESTED

1 Give an example of an object that moves in an oscillating motion. [1 mark]
2 Give an example of a second-order lever. [1 mark]
3 Explain what is meant by torque. [2 marks]
4 Explain how a cam and follower mechanism works and the types of motion it transmits. [3 marks]
5 Describe the speed of motion and size of torque in a pulley and belt system that has a small driver pulley and a larger driven pulley. [2 marks]

6 Materials and their working properties

Papers and boards

- Papers and boards are used to manufacture a wide range of products.
- They are made from **cellulose** fibres found in plants, which is a **renewable** source.
- Papers and boards are usually made from part-**recycled** materials.
- The properties of paper and board can be changed to make it a more useful material (waterproofing, for example).
- Paper is measured from A0 to A6 and in grams per square metre (gsm). Anything weighing less than 200 gsm is classified as paper.
- Boards are always heavier than 200 gsm.
- Corrugated card is a lightweight yet strong material as it contains a fluted structure in the middle layer. It is used for packaging for this reason.

Cellulose: fibres found in plant materials.

Renewable: a source of material that if managed responsibly will not run out.

Recycled: material which has had another use or purpose previously and has been reprocessed and made into a new product.

Table 6.1 Papers and their uses

Paper	Properties	Common uses
Bleed proof	Smooth paper, often used with water and spirit-based markers Prevents marker bleed (when ink runs and seeps through the paper)	Used for presentation drawings
Cartridge paper	Good quality white paper often with a slight texture Available in different weights	Due to the good-quality surface, it can be used for paints and markers as well as drawing
Grid	Paper printed with different grids as guidelines (These can be isometric or differently-sized grids.)	Quick model making and working drawings
Layout paper	Thin translucent lightweight paper Can be drawn on with markers and takes colours well	Initial quick sketching and tracing
Tracing paper	Thin, transparent paper	Tracing copies of drawings

Table 6.2 Boards and their uses

Board	Properties	Common uses
Corrugated card	Strong, lightweight material Made up of two or more layers and a fluted middle section leading to good insulating properties Available in different thicknesses	Packaging such as pizza boxes and large boxes used for heavy items that need protecting
Duplex board	Thin board which often has one side that is suitable for printing	Food packaging
Foil-lined board	Board covered on one side with aluminium foil, making it a good insulator of heat	Takeaway or ready-meal packaging
Foam-core board	Two pieces of board with a core of foam to increase the thickness Thick board that is very lightweight	Model making, such as architectural models
Inkjet card	Treated so it can be used in all inkjet printers	Printing in inkjet printers
Solid white board	Top quality cardboard, smooth and white Good for printing on	Book covers

Exam practice answers at **www.hoddereducation.co.uk/6 myrevisionnotesdownloads**

Natural and manufactured timbers

Timber is a natural product that has the benefit of being renewable. By understanding the properties of different types of timber you will be able to make an informed choice on which one to use when designing and making products.

- Natural timber is categorised into two groups: **hardwoods** and **softwoods**.
- Hardwoods come from deciduous trees that have broad leaves that generally fall in autumn.
- Hardwoods are generally harder, more expensive, more durable and take longer to grow than softwoods.

Table 6.3 Types of hardwood

Hardwood	Properties	Common uses
Ash	Tough and flexible Wide grained Finishes well	Sports equipment, ladders
Beech	Hard and strong Close grain Prone to warping and splitting	Furniture, children's toys, workshop tool handles and bench tops
Mahogany	Strong and durable Available in wide planks Fairly easy to work but can have interlocking grain	Good quality furniture, panelling and veneers
Oak	Hard, tough and durable Open grain Can be finished to a high standard	Timber framed buildings, high quality furniture, flooring
Balsa	Strong and durable Lightweight, easy to work	Model making, floats and rafts

- Softwoods come from coniferous trees that have needle type leaves and keep their leaves all year.
- Softwoods are generally easier to work and, as they grow faster than hardwoods, are considered to be more sustainable than hardwoods.

Table 6.4 Types of softwood

Softwood	Properties	Common uses
Larch	Reddish in colour and has a striking grain pattern Tough but easy to work, although quite resinous and prone to splitting Naturally resistant to rot	Fencing, fence posts, cladding and decking
Pine	Straight grained, light yellow in colour Soft and easy to work Can be quite knotty	Interior joinery and furniture, window frames
Spruce	Creamy white in colour Easy to work with small knots Lightweight with good resonant properties	Bedroom furniture, stringed musical instruments

Manufactured boards – timber which is manufactured into large boards by either laminating or by compression.

Advantages over natural timber:

- available in large sheets: 2,440 mm by 1,220 mm (8 ft x 4 ft)
- stable, less likely to warp, twist, shrink or bow
- smooth, flat surface
- suited to CNC machining.

> **Hardwoods**: come from deciduous trees and are generally hard and durable.
>
> **Softwoods**: come from coniferous trees that are relatively fast growing.
>
> **Manufactured boards**: man-made boards that come in large sizes and are usually flat and stable.

Table 6.5 Types of manufactured boards

Manufactured board	Description	Properties
Medium density fibreboard (MDF)	Made from compressed fine wood fibres bonded together with resin	This board is relatively inexpensive and has a flat, smooth surface
Plywood	Made from wood veneers glued together with alternating grain	Very strong, with a flat, smooth surface
Chipboard	Made from wood chips bonded together with resin	Inexpensive construction material

Metals and alloys

REVISED

Metal is a naturally-occurring material that is found in the ground in the form of ore. It is non-renewable but generally easy to recycle. Different metals have very different properties and are categorised into **ferrous** and **non-ferrous** metals.

Table 6.6 Ferrous metals

Ferrous metal	Composition	Properties	Common uses
Low carbon steel (mild steel)	Iron and 0.15–0.35% carbon	Good tensile strength, tough, malleable Poor resistance to corrosion	Car bodies, nuts, bolts, and screws, RSJs and girders
Cast iron	Iron and 3.5% carbon	Hard surface but has a brittle soft core Strong compressive strength Cheap	Vices, car brake discs, cylinder blocks, manhole covers
High carbon steel (tool steel)	Iron and 0.70–1.4% carbon	Hard but also brittle Less tough, malleable or ductile than medium carbon steel	Screwdrivers, chisels, taps and dies

Table 6.7 Non-ferrous metals

Non-ferrous metal	Properties	Common uses
Aluminium	Lightweight, soft, ductile and malleable A good conductor of heat and electricity Corrosion-resistant	Aircraft bodies, high-end car chassis, cans, cooking pans, bike frames
Copper	Extremely ductile and malleable An excellent conductor of heat and electricity Easily soldered and corrosion-resistant	Plumbing fittings, hot water tanks, electrical wire
Tin	Soft, ductile and malleable Low melting point Excellent corrosion resistance	Coatings on food and drinks cans, solders

Exam practice answers at **www.hoddereducation.co.uk/6 myrevisionnotesdownloads**

Non-ferrous metal	Properties	Common uses
Zinc	Weak in its pure state High level of corrosion resistance Low melting point Easily worked	As a galvanised coating in crash barriers, corrugated roofing, intricate die-cast products

- **Alloys** can be ferrous or non-ferrous.

Table 6.8 Alloys

Alloy	Composition	Properties	Common uses
Brass – non-ferrous alloy	Alloy of copper (65%) and zinc (35%)	Strong and ductile Casts well Corrosion-resistant Conductor of heat and electricity	Castings, forgings, taps, wood screws
Stainless steel – ferrous alloy	Alloy of steel also including chromium (18%), nickel (8%) and magnesium (8%)	Hard and tough Excellent resistance to corrosion	Sinks, cutlery, surgical equipment, homewares
Duralumin	Alloy of aluminum (90%), copper (4%), magnesium (1%), manganese (0.5–1%)	Strong, soft and malleable Excellent corrosion resistance Lightweight	Aircraft structure and fixings, suspension applications, fuel tanks

Ferrous metals: metals that contain iron, are magnetic but are prone to rusting.

Non-ferrous metals: metals that do not contain iron and therefore do not rust.

Alloy: a mixture of two or more metals designed to improve the quality of the metal for a given purpose.

Polymers

REVISED

The majority of polymers that we use are refined from crude oil. This means that they are non-renewable but many are recyclable. Polymers are categorised into **thermoforming polymers** and **thermosetting polymers**.

- Thermoforming polymers have the advantage of being able to be repeatedly formed and reformed with the use of heat.
- They can have additives to improve their working properties, and pigments added to alter their appearance.

Table 6.9 Thermoforming polymers

Thermoforming polymer	Properties	Common uses
Acrylic (PMMA)	Hard Excellent optical quality Good resistance to weathering Scratches easily	Car-light units, bath tubs, shop signage and displays
High impact polystyrene (HIPS)	Tough, hard and rigid Good impact resistance Lightweight	Children's toys, yoghurt pots, refrigerator liners

Thermoforming polymer	Properties	Common uses
High-density polythene (HDPE)	Hard and stiff Excellent chemical resistance	Washing-up bowls, buckets, milk crates, bottles and pipes
Polypropylene (PP)	Tough Good heat and chemical resistance Lightweight Fatigue-resistant	Toys, DVD and Blu-ray cases, food packaging film, bottle caps and medical equipment
Polyvinyl chloride (PVC)	Hard and tough Good chemical and weather resistance Low cost Can be rigid or flexible	Pipes, guttering, window frames
Polyethylene terephthalate (PET)	Tough and durable Lightweight Food safe Impermeable to water Low cost	Drinks bottles, food packaging

- Thermosetting polymers can also be shaped and formed with heat, but once set they cannot be reshaped. Unfortunately, this makes them very difficult to recycle.

Table 6.10 Thermosetting polymers

Thermosetting polymer	Properties	Common uses
Epoxy resin	Electrical insulator Good chemical and wear resistance	Adhesives such as Araldite™, PCB component encapsulation
Melamine formaldehyde (MF)	Stiff, hard and strong Excellent resistance to heat, scratching and staining	Kitchen work-surface laminates, tableware
Phenol formaldehyde (PF)	Hard Heat- and chemical-resistant Good electrical insulator Limited colours available	Electrical fittings, saucepan handles, bowling balls
Polyester resin	Brittle but becomes tough when laminated with glass fibre Hard and resistant to UV	GRP boats, car body panels
Urea formaldehyde (UF)	Stiff and hard Heat-resistant Good electrical insulator	White electrical fittings, toilet seats, adhesive used in MDF

> **Thermoforming polymers**: polymers that can be formed and shaped with the use of heat.
>
> **Thermosetting polymers**: polymers that once formed cannot be reformed with the use of heat.

Exam practice answers at **www.hoddereducation.co.uk/6 myrevisionnotesdownloads**

Textiles

Fabrics and textiles are used for much more than clothing and there are many different types of fibre and fabric available.

The starting point for all fabrics is the fibre, which is a very fine, hair-like structure, and the fibre's properties will vary depending on where it comes from.

Designers need to be aware of the different fabrics when selecting one for a specific product.

- **Natural fibres** come from plants (for example, cotton) and animals (for example, wool and silk).

Table 6.11 **Natural fibres**

Cotton	Good strength, very absorbent, creases and shrinks, poor insulator, very flammable
Wool	Moderate strength, very absorbent, good crease-resistance, can shrink badly, good insulator, not very flammable
Silk	Good strength, very absorbent, can crease badly but natural elasticity helps it shed creases, warm and cool to wear, not very flammable

- **Synthetic fibres** are made from oil-based chemicals (for example, polyester, nylon and elastane).

Table 6.12 **Synthetic fibres**

Polyamide	Very strong and abrasion-resistant, non-absorbent, does not crease or shrink, slight elasticity, poor insulator, melts but does not burn, **thermoplastic**
Polyester	Very strong and abrasion-resistant, non-absorbent, does not crease or shrink, no elasticity, poor insulator, melts but does not burn, thermoplastic
Elastane	Good strength, non-absorbent, does not crease or shrink, very high elasticity, poor insulator, does not burn

- **Blended fabrics** are often used to get the best out of each fibre. Polyester is often blended with cotton and other fibres as it reduces absorbency, creasing and shrinking, and adds strength and thermoplastic qualities to the fabric.
- Woven textiles: the plain weave is the simplest structure and makes strong fabrics with a smooth surface that is good for printing on.
- **Non-woven fabrics** are made directly from layers of fibres and include felt and bonded fabrics.
- Bonded fabrics are made from webs of fibres held together in various ways.
- Felts are made using the natural felting ability of wool fibres.
- Knitted fabrics are made of interlocked loops of yarn.

Natural fibres: fibres from plant and animal sources.

Synthetic fibres: fibres manufactured from oil-based chemicals.

Thermoplastic fibres: these soften when heated and can be heat-set into new shapes.

Blended fabrics: containing two or more different fibres.

Non-woven fabrics: these are made directly from fibres without the need to make them into yarns first.

Exam tip

When asked to give an example of a fibre or fabric for a specific use, think about the qualities needed in the product, such as strength or absorbency, to help you choose one that is right. It might help to remember that natural fibres have almost the opposite qualities to synthetic fibres. For example, natural fibres are good at absorbing moisture but synthetic fibres are almost totally non-absorbent.

Typical mistake

Many students confuse woven and knitted structures; the yarns in woven fabrics are interlaced but are looped together in knitted fabrics.

Table 6.13 Fabric Structures

Woven fabrics	Little stretch, usually have good strength, poor insulators, can crease easily, can fray
Non-woven fabrics	Poor stretch, poor strength, poor insulators, poor crease-resistance, do not fray
Knitted fabrics	Good stretch, moderate strength, good insulators in still air but poor in moving air, have good resistance to creasing, do not fray but weft knit structure can ladder

Material properties

REVISED

Material properties need to be considered to select the correct material for the job.

A material's physical properties describe how that material will behave under specific conditions.

● Absorbency – how well a material soaks up and retains liquids, heat or light. This is an important property of most fabrics.

● Density – a material's mass per unit volume.

● Fusibility – how easily a material's state can be turned into a liquid (solder melts with the heat of a soldering iron due to a low melting point).

● Electrical conductivity – how easily electrical energy can be passed through a material (for example, gold is an excellent conductor).

● Thermal conductivity – how easily a material allows heat to pass through it. (Aluminium has good thermal conductivity and is used in pans.)

A material's mechanical properties describe how it will behave when being worked or shaped.

● Strength – a material's ability to withstand a constant force without breaking. Strength is linked to the five forces that can act upon a material (tension, compression, torsion, shear and bending).

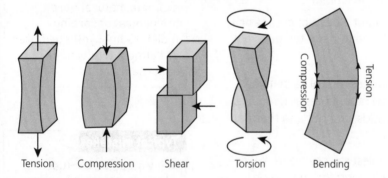

Figure 6.1 Forces

- Hardness – the ability to withstand scratching, cutting and abrasion. (Melamine is used for kitchen work surfaces due to its hardness.)
- Toughness – a material's ability to withstand impact. (HDPE is used to make toys due to its toughness).
- Malleability – a material's ability to be permanently deformed or shaped by impact, rolling or pressing, without breaking. (Low carbon steel is used on car body panels as they can be pressed into shape.)
- Ductility – the ability to be pulled or drawn into a fine wire without breaking. (Copper used to make wire is ductile).
- Elasticity – a material's ability to be stretched under force and to return to its original shape. (Lycra is used in sportswear as it can stretch to fit the body.)

Typical mistake

Don't mix up the categories of the different types of materials – such as stating that oak is a softwood, brass is a pure ferrous metal, or acrylic (PMMA) is a thermosetting polymer.

Exam tip

Make sure that you can visually identify materials from a photograph and that you know the properties and uses of a range of different woods, metals, polymers and textiles.

Now test yourself

TESTED

1 Give the name of a paper/board used for packaging and the properties which make it suitable. [2 marks]
2 For a mechanical and a physical property of your choice, give a definition of each and an example of a material that has that property. [4 marks]
3 List three features of a coniferous tree. [3 marks]
4 Name a suitable polymer for a water bottle. [1 mark]
5 Explain why most aircraft are made using aluminium. [3 marks]
6 What is the source of synthetic fibres? [1 mark]
7 Give three reasons why fibres are often blended before being made into a fabric. [3 marks]

Exam practice

1 Which of these statements is true?
   a) Cotton fibres are very flammable.
   b) Polyester is an absorbent fibre.
   c) Polyester fibres are very elastic.
   d) Wool fibres come from a plant. [1 mark]

2 Give the correct definition for the term 'hardness'.
   a) The ability to withstand bending
   b) The ability to withstand impact
   c) The ability to withstand scratching
   d) The ability to withstand twisting [1 mark]

3 Which of the following explains why corrugated card is used in packaging?
   a) It is aesthetically pleasing.
   b) It is inexpensive.
   c) It is lightweight.
   d) It is waterproof. [1 mark]

4 Which of the following fibres is thermoplastic?
   a) Cotton   c) Silk
   b) Polyamide   d) Wool [1 mark]

5 Which of the following is not a type of weave?
   a) Plain   c) Twill
   b) Satin   d) Weft [1 mark]

6 Describe a way to enhance the properties of paper/card. [1 mark]
7 State two reasons why polyamide fabrics are used for car seatbelts. [2 marks]
8 Name two staple fibres. [2 marks]
9 State two reasons why wool fabrics can be unpopular with consumers. [2 marks]
10 State two reasons why elastane fibres are used in swimwear fabrics. [2 marks]
11 State two reasons why fabrics made from a blend of cotton and polyester fibres are dangerous when set alight. [2 marks]
12 Name the four types of mechanical motion. [4 marks]
13 Describe what is meant by the term 'finite resource'. [1 mark]
14 Give two advantages of using corn starch polymers. [2 marks]
15 What is a composite material? [2 marks]
16 Name two electronic/mechanical input devices. [2 marks]
17 Draw a parallel motion linkage. [2 marks]
18 Give the properties of balsa and suggest a possible use. [3 marks]
19 Give a definition of the term 'ferrous metal'. [1 mark]
20 Give the properties of stainless steel and suggest a possible use. [3 marks]
21 Which one of the following is a thermoforming polymer?
   a) Acrylic (PMMA)   c) Polyester resin
   b) Epoxy resin   d) Phenol formaldehyde [1 mark]

ONLINE

7 Selection of materials and components

There are many different types of fabrics and textile materials available to designers and choosing the right one for a commercially-manufactured product is very important if it is to be successful with consumers. Designers and manufacturers must understand the wants and needs of the target market and be aware of the many different qualities of textile materials so that they can make appropriate choices.

Selection of materials and components

REVISED ☐

Many factors will affect the choice of fabrics and components for textile products. These will be of greater or less importance for different products and at different times. When selecting a fabric for a product, the designer must think about:

Functionality

- How the fabric performs – what are the most important qualities needed for it to suit the particular product that is to be made?
- Does it need to be strong, absorbent or water-resistant, warm or cool, windproof, flame-retardant, easy to care for, resistant to chemical and biological attack?

Aesthetics

- How important is the appearance or feel of the fabric for the product?
- What are the current fashion trends?

Environmental factors

- What impact will the source and manufacture, use, care and disposal of the fibres, fabrics and components used to make the product have on the environment?
- Is it possible to use different materials that have been made in a way that does not harm the environment?

Availability

- Is the material readily available in the quantities needed?

Cost

- Is the choice of material cost-effective and within the allotted budget?

Social factors

- Are the materials used or manufacturing methods likely to have an adverse effect on the lives of anyone involved?

Cultural factors

- Will the product fit in with the cultural values and norms of the target market group? Is it likely to cause offence to any groups of people?

Ethical factors

- What is the likely ethical impact of making and using the product?
- Will it have a negative effect on the lives of any humans or animals?

Exam practice answers at **www.hoddereducation.co.uk/6 myrevisionnotesdownloads**

8 Forces and stresses

Forces and stresses

Fabrics often need to be strengthened or reinforced so that they do not stretch, lose their shape or break during use. Some examples are:

- using **interfacing** behind buttons and buttonholes and pockets to strengthen the fabric
- interfacing a skirt/trouser waistband or a neckline to stop the fabric stretching
- putting interfacing in a collar or cuffs to stiffen them and help them hold their shape
- making a tightly-woven fabric such as webbing from synthetic fibres.

> **Interfacing**: a woven or non-woven fabric used as an extra layer to give additional strength and help to keep the shape of a textile product.

9 Ecological and social footprint

The main effects of the textile industry concern the use of natural resources such as energy and water, and the use of toxic chemicals during the sourcing and processing of fibres and fabrics and the impact of this on the environment and people's lives. There are many ways that manufacturers are trying to reduce the damage.

Ecological issues in the design and manufacture of products

- Growing cotton needs lots of chemical fertilisers and insecticides.
- This can harm workers' health and uses large quantities of water that may be needed for drinking water.
- The intensive farming and deforestation of land for cotton crops causes changes to the landscape and destroys habitats.
- Transporting textile materials and products from where they were made to the country where they are to be sold uses fuel and puts pressure on transport systems.
- Textile waste takes up a lot of landfill space and toxic chemicals can leech out into surrounding land and waterways.
- Components using energy in their manufacture, and some metals and plastics (for example, those used for zips and buttons) may have a toxic effect on the environment.
- Colouring processes use a lot of chemicals and water, and their effluent can pollute waterways.
- The use of chemical finishes such as flame retardancy can cause pollution of waterways and land if waste is not disposed of properly.

Figure 9.1 This shirt will have interfacing in the collar to help it hold its shape, and in the pocket flaps and behind the buttons and buttonholes to strengthen the fabric

The six Rs

- Synthetic fibres are made from petrochemicals which come from non-renewable sources.
- Synthetic fibres take many years to decompose, but polyester fabrics can be recycled or made from recycled plastic bottles.
- **Ingeo™** is a biodegradable fibre that can be used to replace polyester.
- Reusing, recycling and repairing textile products can help reduce the waste sent to landfill.
- Rethink whether it is really necessary to buy textile products, especially fashion products, that are used very few times before being thrown away.

Social issues in the design and manufacture of products

- Using **organic cotton** is better for the environment and has less impact on workers' lives and health but is more expensive.
- More sustainable **regenerated fibres** such as Tencel® and Modal® can be used to replace cotton.

Figure 9.2 Polyester fleece can be made from recycled plastic bottles

- Carbon emissions can be reduced by making products nearer to where they are to be sold and using more ecological forms of transport and fuel.
- It is possible to grow cotton fibres already coloured, reducing the need to use water and chemical dyes.
- Newer, disperse dyes use very little water in their application and do not wash out of the fabric during laundering.
- Ensure that workers in the textile industry are treated fairly.

Ingeo™: a high-performance, biodegradable fibre made from corn starch.

Organic cotton: cotton grown with fewer chemical pesticides and fertilisers than standard cotton.

Regenerated fibres: fibres made by chemically modifying cellulose from spruce trees or cotton linters.

10 Sources and origins

Sources and origins

- Fibres are the starting point of textile materials.
- The table below gives the main information about the sources of different fibres.

Table 10.1 **Fibre sources and origins**

Fibre	Source	Fibre type	Manufacture
Cotton	Natural cellulose from cotton plant	Staple	Flat, ribbon-like fibres are cleaned and twisted together.
Wool	Natural protein from sheep and other animals	Staple	Sheep are sheared and fibres are cleaned and twisted together.
Silk	Natural protein from cocoon of silk caterpillar	Filament	Two triangular-shaped filaments are held together with natural gum from the caterpillar.
Polyester, polyamide and elastane	Petrochemicals from coal or oil	Filament	Chemicals are made into a polymer which is melted then spun into smooth continuous fibres.

- Fibres need to be spun into yarns before they can be made into woven or knitted fabrics.
- Staple fibres are **carded** so that they lie in the same direction before they are twisted (spun) together to make a yarn.
- Filament fibres are lightly twisted together to make a yarn.
- **Spinning** holds the fibres together and adds strength to the yarn.
- If fibres are tightly twisted, the yarn will be strong and smooth but trap less air, so will not insulate as well as a less tightly twisted yarn.
- Filament yarns must be cut down to staple form if they are going to be blended with a staple fibre.

> **Carded**: combing staple fibres so that they all lie parallel to each other ready for spinning into a yarn.
>
> **Spinning**: twisting fibres together to make a yarn.

11 Using and working with textile-based materials

Properties of textile materials

- The combination of the fibres used, the type of yarn and the way the fabric is made, as well as any fabric pattern or special finishes that may be added, will affect the properties of a textile material.
- When selecting a fabric for a particular application all of these factors must be taken into consideration, as well as the most important properties needed in the product, so that an appropriate choice can be made.
- Patterns on fabrics, such as checks and stripes, usually need to be matched when making a product; this may mean that extra fabric needs to be bought.
- Large patterns do not usually work well on small products.
- Specialised fabrics are often used for sportswear, including:
  - fabrics containing elastane, which give stretch needed for activities such as swimming
  - Polartec® fleece for lightweight thermally insulating garments
  - lightweight, breathable fabrics made from polyester or polyamide **microfibres**, used for active sportswear garments
  - moisture-management fabrics, for example, Coolmax®, used for active sportswear
  - breathable and windproof, waterproof fabrics such as Gore-Tex® used for outdoor sports.
- Specialised fabrics are often used for furnishings, including:
  - fabrics with a flame-retardant finish for upholstery and curtains
  - water-repellent fabrics used for outdoor/garden furnishings
  - fabrics with a sanitised finish used for hospital bedding
  - light-resistant fabrics used for curtains
  - PVC-coated fabrics used for tablecloths.

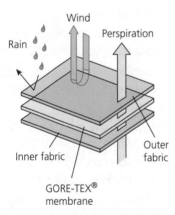

Figure 11.1 The Gore-Tex® membrane stops wind and rain passing through a garment but allows perspiration out

The modification of properties for specific purposes

- Flame-retardancy is an important safety finish.
- Proban and Pyrovatex are chemicals used to give a flame-retardant finish on fabrics made from cellulosic fibres.
- The flame-retardant finish forms an insoluble cross-linked polymer inside the fibres so will not wash out.
- Fabrics made from synthetic fibres are inherently flame-retardant but can cause serious burns when they melt.
- Flame-retardancy is very important for children's nightwear and furnishing fabrics.
- Kevlar and Nomex are very strong heat-resistant fabrics used in protective clothing for motorcycle and racing car drivers.

> **Microfibres**: very fine fibres – 60 times finer than human hair – made from polyamide or polyester.
>
> **Microencapsulated**: fibres with nano-sized chemical capsules in the fibre structure. Rubbing activates the capsules, which release their contents.

- Neoprene – a synthetic rubber – is used for wetsuits.
- **Microencapsulated** fabrics that contain insect and odour repellents.
- Interactive fabrics containing conductive fibres such as carbon, silver and steel allow fabrics to have wearable electronics such as GPS, solar panels and performance monitors.

Shaping and forming using cutting, abrasion and addition

 REVISED

- Fabric is a flat, sheet-form material and needs to be cut and shaped into products.
- Accuracy when cutting the fabric into the required shapes is essential to ensure a high-quality product.
- It is important that the fabric is clean and free of creases before use.
- A pattern **template** is used to ensure that the fabric is cut to the correct size and shape for the product.
- The grainline is a very important marking shown on the pattern template.
- It is important to place the grainline on the straight grain of the fabric, otherwise the fabric will not hang correctly in the finished product.
- This must be checked with a tape measure or ruler for accuracy.
- When folding fabric to get a double layer, both selvedges must be placed exactly on top of each other to keep the grain correct on both layers.
- The pattern must be pinned flat to the fabric at regular intervals to stop it moving as the fabric is cut and so ensure accuracy.
- There are many markings on the pattern that need to be transferred to the fabric to show how the product is to be made and indicate the position of various features such as pockets and buttonholes.
- The markings can be transferred using tailor's chalk, a tracing wheel and tracing paper, or tailor's tacks.

Sewing

- Fabrics can be sewn together using hand or machine stitches.
- Tacking is temporary stitching that is used to hold fabric together until it is ready to be sewn permanently, or to test out an idea.
- The product is permanently sewn together using a seam.
- Seams need to be appropriate for the fabric used, the type of product being made and whether it needs to be hidden or is used as a decorative feature.
- The three main seams are:
  ○ A plain seam is flat and not seen on the outside of the product, but the seam edges will need to be neatened to stop them fraying.

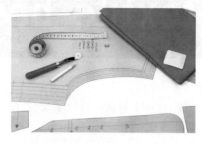

Figure 11.2 Pattern templates must be placed and cut accurately before transferring pattern markings to the fabric

> **Template**: a pattern shape, usually made from paper or card, used to cut out fabric to the size and shape required.

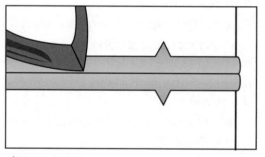

a) Plain seam

Stitch plain seam 10 mm from edge. Trim seam allowance to 3 mm.

Turn to right side. Press flat. Stitch exactly on the seamline 5 mm away.

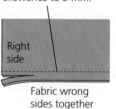

Right side

Fabric wrong sides together

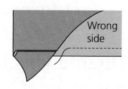

Wrong side

b) French seam

Press 5 mm under

Place fabric wrong sides together and stitch on seamline.

Press seam open. Trim one seam allowance to 5 mm.

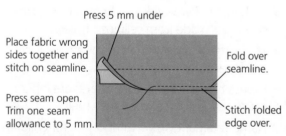

Fold over seamline.

Stitch folded edge over.

c) Double-machined seam

Figure 11.3 The three main types of seam used to permanently join fabric together

Exam practice answers at **www.hoddereducation.co.uk/6 myrevisionnotesdownloads**

○ A French seam is sewn twice so all the edges are enclosed and it is not visible on the outside of the product. It is a strong seam useful for fine fabrics as the turnings are hidden, but it can be bulky on thicker fabrics.

○ The double-stitched seam is strong and flat with all the turnings enclosed. It is visible on the outside of the product so is often used as a decorative feature.

Two-dimensional fabric can be shaped to make a three-dimensional product. The main ways of doing this are by using:

Pleats

- Pleats are folds in fabric that are stitched or pressed in place.
- They allow for movement in clothing and add texture and a decorative effect.

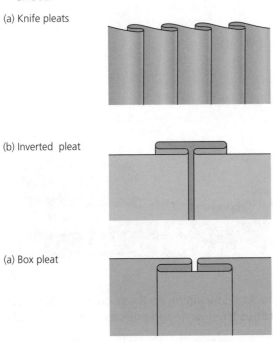

(a) Knife pleats

(b) Inverted pleat

(a) Box pleat

Figure 11.4 The three main types of pleat

- The three main types of pleat are:
  ○ knife pleats (single folds all facing the same way)
  ○ inverted pleats (two knife pleats facing each other)
  ○ box pleats (two knife pleats facing away from each other).
- Tucks are similar to pleats but narrower and stitched along their length, used as a decorative feature.

Gathering

- Fabric is drawn up using thread to reduce the length of fabric.
- Gathers are used to shape fabric, add ease and movement in clothing and add a decorative effect.

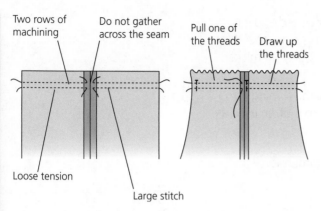

Two rows of machining

Do not gather across the seam

Pull one of the threads

Draw up the threads

Loose tension

Large stitch

Figure 11.5 Gathering is used to shape fabric and add a decorative effect

Quilting

- Quilting adds texture and decoration to a product.
- Quilted fabric consists of a layer of wadding sandwiched between two layers of fabric.
- The layers are stitched together in a pattern.
- Quilting adds warmth as the trapped air in the wadding is an insulator.

Figure 11.6 Quilting can add texture and volume to a garment and is decorative and insulating

Figure 11.7 The piping on these cushions protects the edges from wear and adds a decorative touch

Piping

- Piping defines and strengthens an edge and can add decoration.
- It is made by enclosing a cord in a strip of bias-cut fabric before stitching it into a seam.

12 Stock forms, types and sizes

Stock forms, types and sizes

It is helpful to know the standard forms and sizes of textile materials when planning the manufacture of a product, so that appropriate and cost-efficient choices can be made.

- Yarns are made by twisting fibres together.
- Yarns are twisted with other yarns to make them stronger so they can be used for many purposes – this is called **plying**.
- The ply of a yarn refers to the number of single strands in the yarn.
- Fabrics are made in a limited number of widths.
- The fabric width will determine the amount needed to make a product – the wider the fabric, usually the less needs to be bought.
- General-purpose sewing threads are mostly made from polyester fibre.
- They are dyed in many different colours so that they can be matched to fabric colours. Embroidery threads are made from many different fibres and some are designed to give special effects.
- There are many different fastenings including zips, buttons, Velcro, poppers, press studs, and hooks and eyes.
- Fastenings are available in a wide range of different types, sizes and colours.

> **Plying**: twisting two or more single yarns together to make a multi-ply yarn.

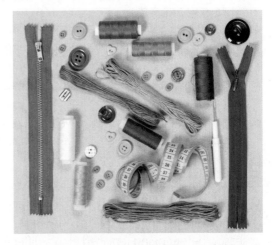

Figure 12.1 Many different types of thread and fastenings are available in a range of stock forms

13 Scales of production

- The manufacturing method used to make textile products depends on the number of products required.
- Many textile products are fashion items, which have a fairly short life when compared to other products.
- Many may be made over a limited period of time and then not made again.
- The main production methods used are:

One-off manufacture (prototype)

REVISED

- This may be a **prototype** to test the design or plan the manufacture when the product goes into quantity manufacture.
- **One-off manufacture** is used to make unique garments and other products for an individual customer, such as a wedding dress or a made-to-measure suit. These are often called bespoke garments.
- One-off manufacture is expensive because it is labour-intensive and products are usually made to a very high standard.

> **Prototype**: an early sample, model, or release of a product, made to test a concept or a process.
>
> **One-off manufacture**: manufacture in which only one complete product is made.

Batch production

REVISED

- Because fashions change quickly, most textile products are **batch** manufactured. For example, a summer top will only be sold over one season before being replaced with a different style, so although many will be made in a range of sizes, the manufacture will quickly change to a different style.
- Workers are skilled in the use of different machines and processes, so can easily change from making one type of product to a different one when fashions change.
- Modern manufacturing systems use computer control to keep track of what is made and to help to change to a new product quickly, according to consumer demand.

> **Batch production**: production in which a limited number of the same product is made during a particular period of time.
>
> **Mass production**: manufacturing in large quantities over a long period of time.

Mass production

REVISED

- This uses production lines where different workers make small sections of the product or assemble parts made on a **sub-assembly** line.
- Although specialist machines are used, the workers are usually unskilled.
- This method of production is only used for textile products that do not change much over time, for example, school shirts or duvet covers.

> **Sub-assembly**: a separate manufacturing line that makes small sections of a product, for example collars, ready to add to the product being made.

Exam practice answers at **www.hoddereducation.co.uk/6 myrevisionnotesdownloads**

14 Specialist techniques and processes

Using production aids

Templates

These are frequently used when making textile products, to help make sure that the different parts are cut to the right shape and size.

Using a template helps to ensure that the product is made accurately over and over again.

Patterns

- In the school workshop or the home, commercial patterns that come with instructions for making the product are often used.
- Patterns can also be found in sewing magazines and on the internet.
- They can also be developed on a CAD program from an existing product or **basic blocks**.
- In commercial clothes manufacture, patterns are developed from basic blocks in **standardised sizes**.
- The pattern maker develops the basic shapes by adding style details and other features as required for the design.

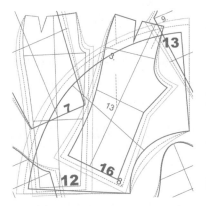

Figure 14.1 Patterns can be traced from sewing magazines

> **Typical mistake**
>
> Don't fall into the trap of thinking that computers make things – they don't!
>
> But they do control many different machines that make things. If you are writing an answer about computer-aided manufacture, give specific examples of how computers are used (for example, making automated buttonholes or computerised embroidery machines). These are specialised machines that are controlled by computers – the computers themselves do not do the sewing.

Figure 14.2 Basic blocks are used as a starting point for patterns in commercial clothes manufacture.

Tools, equipment and processes

- Fabric is cut out in many layers and a computer program places the pattern pieces on the fabric as economically as possible to minimise waste.
- The pattern pieces are held in place by suction, not pins, and the fabric is cut using knives, not scissors.
- Modern computerised systems do not use paper patterns; instead they send the cutting instructions to the cutting machine, and the fabric is cut using lasers or water jets.
- Pattern markings are transferred to fabric using:
  - drill markers to make small holes in the fabric
  - hot notchers to mark the edge of the fabric with small cuts
  - fluorescent-dye markers to mark the surface of the fabric with dye that is only visible under ultraviolet light.

Figure 14.3 Sewing is done by a team of machinists and passed from one worker to another on a conveyor system

- Sewing is done by a team of machinists using industrial machines that work at high speeds.
- In modern factories, work is moved to different machinists as required, using an automated conveyor system.
- In many factories identical operations, such as making buttonholes and embroidered patterns, are done on computer-controlled machines.
- Pressing is done using special tools that use steam, heat and pressure.
- A computer-controlled, body-shaped steam dolly is used to press some garments.
- The dolly is inflated inside the clothes using steam and air, which makes the creases fall out.
- A tunnel finisher is used to press garment such as shirts.
- Pressing can be controlled by different pressing programs stored in the computer's memory.

> **Basic blocks:** a pattern for each part of a garment that will make a basic garment shape when sewn together.
>
> **Standardised sizes:** a set of body measurements that conform to the British Standards Institute (BSI) standard sizing.

Cutting, shaping and forming to a tolerance

REVISED

- Accurate construction of a product is important to make sure that it looks and performs as intended.
- Manufacturers need to know how accurate the different parts of a product need to be so that they will fit together.
- The level of accuracy required is known as the **tolerance level**.
- Accurate tolerances when working with textile materials are less important and often more difficult to achieve than with other materials, as woven and knitted structures have quite a lot of give in them. This makes it difficult to work to very fine tolerances.
- There are often quite large tolerances, between 5 mm and 20 mm, in the size of commercially manufactured garments.
- These large tolerances do not matter as the size and shape of the human body varies so much, even when people are a standard clothing size 10 or 18, and the differences will not be noticed.
- Furnishing products such as duvet covers and cushions are also manufactured to quite large tolerances as an exact size is not critical.
- If a client had an individual made-to-measure garment made, the tolerances would be smaller to give a precise fit.
- Sometimes the individual parts of a product must be made accurately so they will fit together when the product is constructed, for example in patchwork.

> **Tolerance level:** the acceptable variation in the size a product or part of a product, usually given as an upper and a lower limit.

Figure 14.4 Patchwork pieces must be cut and sewn very accurately so that they fit together

Exam practice answers at **www.hoddereducation.co.uk/6 myrevisionnotesdownloads**

Commercial processes

- In modern, commercial manufacture, fabrics and textile products are made in large factories using many automated processes.
- As the manufacture of garments is completed, they are stored on hangers and moveable rails ready to go straight on display in shops. The manufacturer adds tickets and tags to the garments to identify the different styles and sizes. The barcodes on these tickets can be read by the shop's electronic tills, which record which garments are selling and automatically re-order new stock.

Weaving

- Woven fabrics are made on a loom which interlaces two yarns at right angles to each other.
- The warp is fixed in the loom and runs the length of the fabric.
- The second set of yarns – the weft yarns – go horizontally across the loom, weaving in and out of the warp yarns.
- The main actions in the weaving process are:
  - Shedding: the warp yarns pass through heddles that are raised to make a space (called a shed) for the weft threads to pass through.
  - Picking: the weft yarn is carried through the shed in a shuttle, a rapier, a jet of water or a jet of air.
  - Beating: a reed pushes the weft yarn into place.
  - The heddles are lowered to allow the weft to pass under the warp yarns it passed through on the previous row.
  - Let off: the warp yarns are unwound from a beam as the fabric is woven.
  - Take off: the woven fabric is wound onto the cloth beam.
- A shuttle loom is used to make a plain weave and a jacquard loom is used to make complex patterns.

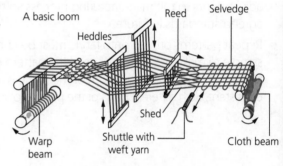

Figure 14.5 A basic weaving loom

Dyeing

The three basic steps involved in **dyeing** are:

1 Immerse the textile in the dye.
2 The dye attaches itself to the fibre.
3 The dye is fixed within the fibre.

> **Dyeing**: the permanent application of colour to a fibre or fabric to give a uniform colour.

The strength with which the dye is held inside the fibre is called colour-fastness.

- Colour may need to be fast to washing (for example, clothing), sunlight (for example, curtains) or rubbing (for example, seating).
- Dye can be added to a textile product at different stages of manufacture:
  - Spin dyeing – the dye is put into the spinning solution of synthetic fibres
  - Stock dyeing – fibres are dyed before being spun into yarn
  - Yarn dyeing – yarns are dyed before being made into fabrics
  - Piece dyeing – the dyeing of fabrics
  - Garment dyeing – made-up garments are dyed according to demand for different colours.

Patterns can be dyed into fabrics by preventing the dye from reaching some parts of the fabric. This is called resist dyeing. Two methods of resist dyeing are:

● Batik – hot wax or flour paste is used to draw a pattern on the fabric before it is dyed
● Tie-dye – the fabric is folded or twisted then tied to stop dye reaching some parts.

(See page 81 for information on printing.)

Quality control

REVISED

● Commercial manufacturers need to make quality control checks at certain stages during production to make sure the products are of the agreed quality.
● These stages are built into the production specification.
● Checking at an appropriate stage is important or it may be too late to correct any mistakes.
● Different sections of a product must be made to the correct dimensions and within the agreed tolerance levels, or they will not fit together accurately.
● A sample of the products will be inspected as they are made and information about the samples will be analysed.
● This feedback makes it possible to trace the reasons for any problems, whether they are caused by machines or operatives, and make adjustments to the manufacturing process so that all products meet the agreed standards in future.
● Repeat patterns printed onto fabric must be checked against the original sample to make sure that the size of the pattern is correct, the repeat along the length and across the width of the fabric is accurate and the colour is consistent, with different parts of the pattern placed accurately on the fabric.

> **Exam tip**
>
> If a question asks about fabric finishes and modified properties, you should explain why they are needed and give examples of their use.

15 Surface treatment and finishes

- Colour and pattern are important aesthetic considerations for consumers and can be added to fabric using dyeing or printing (see page 41 for information on dyeing).
- Before colour can be applied the fabric needs to be cleaned to remove natural impurities and dirt and oil picked up from machines during manufacture, otherwise the colour will not attach itself evenly to the fabric.

Printing

- Patterns can be printed onto fabrics. The dye is made into a thick printing paste so it is easy to apply.
- The advantages of printing are:
  - There are more opportunities for designing.
  - More colours can be used.
  - Complex designs can be produced.
- The main types of fabric printing are:
  - Screen-print: a type of stencilling using a fine mesh stretched over a frame. Parts of the mesh are blocked off to make a pattern and each colour in the design has its own screen. The main types used commercially are rotary, flatbed and carousel screen-printing.
  - Roller print: engraved copper rollers that are the full width of the fabric are coated with printing paste and rolled over the fabric. The circumference of the roller makes one complete pattern repeat and each colour in the print has its own roller. This is a quick but expensive method only used for long print runs.
  - Sublimation print: the design is printed onto a special paper and transferred to fabric using a heat press. The heat turns the dye into a vapour which is transferred to the fabric. This method works best on polyester and other fabrics made from synthetic fibres.
  - Digital print: a pattern is designed on a computer then printed straight onto the fabric. The colour is fixed in the fabric using steam. Digital printing is only suitable for small amounts of fabric.

Stain protection

- Special finishes are sometimes applied to fabric to make them better suited for their intended use.
- Finishes may be used to make the fabric safer, improve the aesthetics, improve the functionality of a fabric and to cancel out some of the negative qualities of the fibres used to make the fabric.
- Stain-resistance is a chemical finish that also makes a fabric water-repellent.
  - The fabric is sprayed with fluorocarbons that stop oil and water-based stains attaching themselves to the fabric so that it stays cleaner for longer.
  - The finishes are environmentally friendly and biodegrade over time.
  - Teflon® and Scotchgard® are the best-known stain-resistant finishes.

Figure 15.1 Teflon® and Scotchgard® finishes makewater and oil-based stains roll off the fabric so the fabric stays clean and dry

Now test yourself

TESTED ☐

1 Describe three different ways that textiles can be made more sustainable. [3 marks]
2 Name three different types of modern textile material used in sportswear. [3 marks]
3 What is the difference between the warp yarns and the weft yarns in a woven fabric? [2 marks]
4 List two reasons why a repeat pattern printed onto fabric is checked against the original design. [2 marks]
5 a) What is the name of the seam shown below? [1 mark]

Figure 15.2

b) List two reasons why it would be used when making jeans. [2 marks]

Exam practice

1 Which of these statements is true?
   a) Bonded fabrics are made from webs of fibres.
   b) The selvedge of a woven fabric runs parallel to the weft yarns.
   c) Warp knitted fabrics are very stretchy.
   d) Weft knitted fabrics will not ladder if a loop is broken.   [1 mark]

2 Which of the following finishes would use microencapsulation?
   a) Crease resistant   c) Insect repellent
   b) Flame retardant   d) Water repellent   [1 mark]

3 Explain what is meant by a sub-assembly line   [3 marks]

4 Give two reasons why interfacing is used in trouser waistbands.   [2 marks]

5 Resist-dyeing techniques such as tie-dye and batik are used to add interest to textile
   products. Use notes and/or sketches to explain one of these techniques in detail. [5 marks]

6 Explain what is meant by the term 'deforestation'.   [1 mark]

7 Give two examples of the consequences of deforestation.   [2 marks]

ONLINE

16 Investigation, primary and secondary data

Research is an essential part of designing and manufacturing products for clients and users. It is collected and used throughout the process, providing essential data and knowledge, which helps to produce a successful end product.

Using primary and secondary data to understand client and/or user needs

- Research allows you to learn more about a subject and make decisions which help the user of the end product.
- Gathering data when you research will help you understand the needs of the client.
- **Primary research** – this means collecting the research information first-hand, for yourself. This can be in the form of questionnaires, interviews, observations and tests.
- **Secondary research** – this means using the research that somebody else has already collected (such as through books, magazines and the internet).

Market research

- This is carried out by manufacturers in order to gain an understanding of the person or people that they think will use their products.
- It can provide an accurate picture of the potential buyer for your product.
- Interviews and questionnaires are usually carried out at a face-to-face meeting.
- Questions are used to find out what people are thinking – this could be an expert or a group of people.
- The types of questions asked can be open or closed questions.
  - Open questions allow the interviewee more freedom in their answer to a question.
  - A closed question is more likely to only be answered with a short 'yes' or 'no' type response.
- Closed-question responses are easier to analyse.
- Designers need to consider **human factors** (issues relating to people), when they begin to design a product.
- Human factors can be categorised as:
  - physiological – the way in which people move and their physical attributes
  - psychological – the way a person reacts to new experiences
  - sociological – the effects a product will have on people.
- The way in which a user interacts with their environment is called **ergonomics**.

Focus groups

- **Focus groups** are also used to collect research, especially by big companies.
- This is a form of primary research and is a useful way of collecting the views of a large group of people.

> **Exam tip**
>
> Be able to analyse data collected as research in the form of graphs, charts and tables.

Anthropometric data and percentiles

- A further example of primary research collected by a designer is **anthropometric** data.
- Measurements are taken from the human body and used to ensure the product fits the intended user or group.
- Graphs like the one below are used to show anthropometric data.
- The designer selects only relevant data which will help them to produce a product to suit the intended target audience.
- Usually those below the 5th percentile and above the 95th percentile are ignored, as these measurements are below and above average.

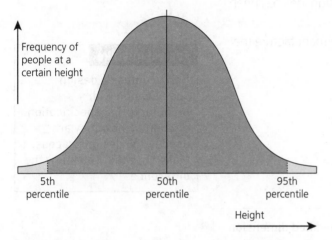

Figure 16.1 A percentile graph showing heights

> **Primary research**: investigations carried out first hand.
>
> **Secondary research**: using the investigations of others.
>
> **Human factors**: issues relating to people.
>
> **Ergonomics**: human interaction with products.
>
> **Focus group**: a large group of people who feed back their opinions.
>
> **Anthropometrics**: human dimensions.

How to write a design brief

REVISED

- A design brief is a statement outlining what is to be designed and made.
- It can be written most simply as 'Design and make …'
- Further details can be added to the brief to include a context and any details that research may have identified already.
- The design brief shows a clear understanding of the task and how problems will be solved.
- When you are given a design brief, you will need to analyse it by posing relevant questions which can then guide further research.

How to produce a design and manufacturing specification

- The design specification sets out the design constraints based on research that has been carried out.
- It is usually written as a list of clear statements relating to what the design must be, must do and must have.
- The design specification is referred to when designing and evaluating design ideas.
- A manufacturing specification contains all of the information needed to make the product and is produced after the final design idea has been developed.
- A manufacturing specification allows a third party to manufacture the product as it contains details about:
  - materials
  - components
  - tools
  - health and safety
  - sequence of making
  - **tolerances**.

> **Tolerance:** the allowable amount of variation of a specified dimension within which quality can still be assured.

> **Typical mistake**
>
> Don't confuse a design specification with a manufacturing specification or confuse how they are used in the design process. Make sure that you know the difference.

Carrying out investigations in order to identify problems and needs

- The design brief may be altered by the designer throughout the process, in light of new problems or information being discovered.
- If further research and testing finds aspects that are critical to the success of the project and without which the project would not work, changes to the design brief should be made.

Now test yourself

1 Give three examples of primary research. [3 marks]
2 Explain the difference between ergonomics and anthropometrics. [2 marks]
3 What information is given in a manufacturing specification to allow a third party to manufacture the product? [3 marks]
4 Name the three categories of human factors considered by a designer. [3 marks]
5 Why might a design brief change throughout the process? [2 marks]

17 Environmental, social and economic challenge

Designing and making products has an impact on the environment. Understanding how to manage that impact is important.

Deforestation

REVISED

- Trees are cut down to make timber/paper-based products and for grazing space for animals.
- Designers and manufacturers have a responsibility to source materials from **sustainably-**managed forests.
- Forest Stewardship Council® (FSC®)-certified products are made with materials from well-managed forests and/or verified and recycled sources.
- To reduce the impact their products have, designers and companies could:
  - use the most appropriate, responsibly sourced species for the application
  - use FSC-certified materials
  - introduce a zero-deforestation policy
  - set targets to maximise the use of recycled wood, pulp and paper.

Figure 17.1 FSC logo

Carbon dioxide levels and global warming

REVISED

- Global warming is the increase in the average temperature of the Earth's atmosphere and oceans, which has been rising over recent years.
- Global warming occurs when carbon dioxide (CO_2) collects in the atmosphere.
- The gases absorb the sunlight reflecting off the Earth's surface and trap heat which is unable to escape. As a result the Earth gets hotter.
- Increased levels of CO_2 and other gases are a result of humans burning **fossil fuels**, vehicles in transport, land clearing and agriculture.
- Global warming is affecting weather patterns and sea levels as the polar ice caps are melting.
- Designers should try to reduce the impact their products have on the environment.

> **Exam tip**
>
> You may be asked to give examples of, either a product that has a negative effect on the environment, or a product that has been redesigned to lessen its impact. Make sure you know of examples that you can discuss at length.

Fair trade

- Fair trade is a trading partnership that works towards fair prices and better working conditions for farmers and workers who produce goods all around the world.
- People gain a fair price for their goods and are protected from **exploitation**.
- Fair trade supports developing communities, helping to protect the environment in which they live and work.
- The fair trade logo found on products shows that ingredients and materials have met fair trade standards.

Figure 17.2 Fair trade logo

Sustainability: design which considers the environmental impact, both in the long and short term.

Fossil fuels: finite resources such as coal, oil and gas.

Exploitation: the action or fact of treating someone unfairly in order to benefit from their work.

> **Typical mistake**
>
> This topic lends itself to discussion in the exam so try to be able to give the pros and cons of an argument and have products and examples to back up your discussion. If you give only basic facts and your argument lacks substance in a discussion-type question, you will not achieve the higher marks.

Now test yourself

1 Explain how global warming is changing the Earth. [4 marks]
2 Give examples of products that would carry the fair trade logo. [2 marks]
3 Explain the importance of using FSC materials in a new product. [3 marks]
4 How does fair trade support workers? [3 marks]
5 Discuss the role a designer plays in minimising the impact on the environment. [6 marks]

18 The work of others

Designers and design movements of the past have been influential in the design of the products we use today. They have changed the way we view products and continue to be a source of inspiration.

Designers

Coco Chanel

- Gabrielle Bonheur 'Coco' Chanel was a French fashion designer.
- Chanel was known for creating a more comfortable style for women at a time when corsets were still being worn.
- In 1925, she introduced the Chanel suit with a collarless jacket and fitted skirt. Both of these designs are still well known today.
- She is most famous for creating the 'little black dress'. This was controversial at the time as it used a colour associated with mourning.
- Chanel was the first designer to produce her own fragrance and today 'Chanel No. 5' is still an iconic product.

William Morris

- William Morris was founder of the Arts and Crafts movement in the nineteenth century and set up his own business in 1861.
- Morris is best known for his highly decorative wallpaper and furnishings, using nature and natural forms to inspire his patterns.
- His furniture designs were hand crafted and **ornate**.
- Morris famously said about design: 'Have nothing in your house that you do not know to be useful, or believe to be beautiful.'

> **Ornate:** highly decorative.

Alexander McQueen

- Alexander McQueen was a London-based, English fashion designer who worked for the Givenchy fashion line and Gucci before starting his own line.
- McQueen pushed the boundaries in fashion and created theatrical shows.
- His designs were known for creating visual impact.

Mary Quant

- London designer Mary Quant wanted fashion to be affordable for the younger generation.
- She is most famous for the white, plastic knee-high boots and tight sweaters of the 1960s.
- Due to the success of her shops, she was soon mass-producing clothing and exporting it to the USA.
- Quant is also famous for the mini skirt, popular in the mid-1960s.

Figure 18.1 Iconic McQueen designs

Vivienne Westwood

- Vivienne Westwood is a British designer and former teacher turned jewellery maker.
- She started selling her designs in the early 1970s.
- She was a very influential designer during this period, introducing frilly shirts and tweed suits.
- Her style was very controversial and differed greatly from the fashion at the time.

Companies

REVISED ☐

Alessi

- Alessi is a family-run design company founded in 1921 by Giovanni Alessi.
- The company is known for producing designer products, from chairs to kitchenware.
- Many iconic designers have worked with Alessi, including Richard Sapper, Ettore Sottsass and Philippe Starck.
- Alessi products place importance on personality and interest, creativity and the use of colour. Often made of metal, they are designed to be mass produced.
- The products are not always the most functional.

Apple

- Apple is famous for producing electronics and computer software.
- The company has produced the iPod, iPhone and Mac personal computer.
- Apple was founded by Steve Jobs, Steve Wozniak and Ronald Wayne in 1976. Also associated with Apple is Jonathan Ive.
- Ive is chief designer and has over 5,000 **patents.** He has won many design awards for his work.
- Apple products are sleek and stylish and the technology they use is fundamental to their successful design.

Braun

- Braun is a German design company, designing small appliances.
- In 1929 Max Braun began making radio components, later producing entire radios.
- His company became one of the biggest in Germany, branching out into other electrical items.
- Braun is known for its functionality and its use of colour during the **pop art** period.
- For 30 years, Dieter Rams was the head of design. Today his work is shown in the Museum of Modern Art in New York.

Dyson

- James Dyson invented the first bagless vacuum cleaner after producing 5,127 **prototypes.**
- The Dyson DC01 used 'cyclone technology' to increase suction.
- Other inventions by Dyson include the contra-rotating washing machine (having two drums inside) and the hand dryer.

Exam tip

You only need to know about two of these designers for the exam. Choose two designers that you are interested in to revise.

Typical mistake

If you don't have a depth of knowledge about two designers and movements, you won't be able to discuss their work in detail. You should be able to make reference to the style of specific products they have designed, knowing enough to be able to form arguments. Superficial facts will not allow you to do this.

Patent: a form of intellectual property which protects a designer's ideas.

Pop art: art based on modern popular culture.

Prototype: a first or initial version of a product.

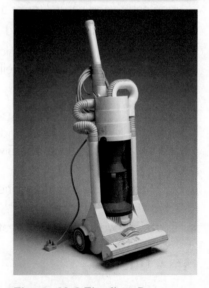

Figure 18.2 The first Dyson vacuum cleaner

Exam tip

You only need to know about two of these companies for the exam. Choose two companies that you are interested in to revise.

Exam practice answers at **www.hoddereducation.co.uk/6 myrevisionnotesdownloads**

Now test yourself

1 For a designer of your choice, list ten facts. [5 marks]
2 Which designers have worked for the design company Alessi and what design are
they most famous for producing? [2 marks]
3 Sketch and explain a product by a designer from the list above. [3 marks]
4 What does the term pop art mean? [1 mark]
5 For a designer of your choice, discuss the reasons that their work is considered iconic. [4 marks]

19 Design strategies

Design strategies give you ways of using imagination and creativity as you start the design process.

Generate imaginative and creative design ideas using a range of different design strategies

Not all successful designs come from professional product designers. Sometimes people see an opportunity and rise to the challenge.

Collaboration – working together

- Large companies such as Rolls Royce have design teams working together to solve problems. Tasks are analysed and solutions explored as a group, sharing ideas.
- Putting everyone's ideas together results in a wider range of resources to choose from as you begin the design process.
- Work that seems daunting to do on your own, such as the **task analysis**, can be easier to do as a group sharing questions and thoughts. For example, at the start of your project you could work collaboratively to analyse a set brief and then move on to answer the questions individually to progress with your project.
- Research for a project can also be carried out collaboratively (for example, visiting a local store to look at existing products). In a group, you can share thoughts and questions about the information you have found.
- Collaborative work can help you gain confidence as you work through your project.

User-centred design

- Problem solving – products are sometimes invented when a problem is discovered. For example, James Dyson's ballbarrow replaces the wheel with a ball to prevent it sinking into mud.
- Client-based approach – when using a client for your project, ensure that they are available to help and support you throughout the process. They should help you to agree the design specification and give feedback on ideas, as well as evaluations.
- Designing through customer feedback – this can help a product to **evolve** when alternative suggestions are put forward. Focus groups can be used to do this when testing a new product.
- Market research companies are available to assist design companies with their research. They use databanks of customers' needs which have been taken from their online searches.

A systems approach

- A system is a group of interconnected parts that does something. Dealing with these parts can be complex, so a 'systems approach' is used.
- What the system is trying to achieve is known as the 'systems goal'.
- 'Systems thinking' involves looking at the whole problem, not just the component parts.
- Systems can be divided into two types:
  - ○ hard systems that are machine- or hardware-dominated
  - ○ soft systems where the actions of humans decide what happens.
- Hard systems are easier to model as they have set behaviours (for example, a switch is either on or off).
- An example of a system is a car. This has lots of interconnected parts but without a driver or fuel it won't work. When there are lots of cars, rules need to be put in place.
- Complex systems can be divided into sub-systems (for example, in a car there is the braking system and steering system).
- Block diagrams can be used to show how a system works.
- Most systems rely on feedback, either negative (keeps a constant) or positive (magnifies something).
- A flow chart is used to show what happens in a system. It uses standard symbols.

Iterative design

- This means using prototypes, testing and analysis to refine a product.
- In your project, client feedback will help to refine design ideas further.
- Modelling will allow you to test out your ideas and help to solve problems, leading to further design development.

Avoiding design fixation

- Use a wide range of sources to help you find inspiration as you start your designs.
- **Geometric** pattern is a good starting point and has been used by many famous designers (such as Mary Quant and Marc Jacobs).
- Geometry is used in both surface patterns and 3D design (for example, the Braun geometrical kettle by Emi Schenkelbach).
- Mathematical patterns are also a starting point. Fibonacci introduced his sequence in 1202. In the Fibonacci sequence, every number after the first two is the sum of the two preceding ones: 0, 1, 1, 2, 3, 5, 8, 13, 21, 34, 55, 89, 144.
- Designing from natural forms – **biomimicry** is an approach which looks to nature for inspiration. Nature has already solved many of the problems that we encounter.
- Shape and pattern in nature can be seen in the work of many famous designers, for example Cath Kidston.
- Natural images can be used to help with your designs but it is useful to adapt the pattern and shape of natural forms.
- Cultural influences – the Great Exhibition took place in London in 1851. It was the first exhibition to celebrate cultural and industrial product design.
- It is now easier to travel and connect through social media and the internet, so we can easily see designs from around the world.

Golden Ratio

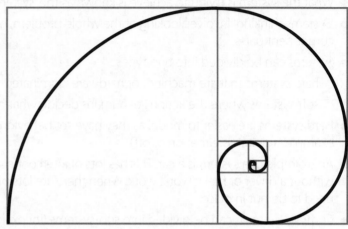

Figure 19.1 **Fibonacci squares**

> **Geometric**: use of shapes and angles in design.

> **Task analysis**: looking at the design task or brief in depth and asking questions.
>
> **Evolve**: to develop gradually.
>
> **Biomimicry**: the design of products modelled on nature.

Explore and develop your own ideas

REVISED ☐

The following design strategies should provide a starting point in designing and developing ideas. You should also consider how social and environmental factors influence design.

Sketching

- Use the best tools available.
- Show different aspects of the design.
- Keep sketches clear and accurate.
- Keep notes simple and precise.
- Spend time designing which aspects of the idea could be improved.
- 3D drawings can help to communicate clearly.

Modelling

- This helps test out ideas quickly and can be done in foam, card, fabric or wire.
- It tests **proportions** and sizes.
- A full-size mock-up in cheaper material can be useful to show construction techniques.
- CAD/CAM makes it quicker to make and change models.
- A full-size mock-up in textiles is called a toile.
- Construction kits can be used to model mechanical systems.
- Electronic systems can be modelled using virtual circuits where component values can be changed and the effect on the circuit tested.

Testing

- Testing should be carried out as you design and manufacture your product.
- Comparison tables and client feedback will help you decide which ideas to develop further.
- You can test the ergonomics of a product to make sure it suits the user.
- Materials and construction methods can also be tested to ensure success.
- In systems, circuits can be tested on prototype boards, known as 'breadboarding', using real components.
- Surface finishes can also be sampled and tested for suitability.

Evaluation of work to improve outcomes

- Along with testing, you will need to:
  - evaluate results
  - carry out improvements
  - refine your design.
- Your design specification can be used as a checklist to help you evaluate and should continue to be used as your project progresses.
- It is useful in your **summative** evaluation to compare your prototype to other similar products on the market.
- Be critical as you evaluate – this will help your product to improve as you develop it.
- Ask your client to test and evaluate your end product.

> **Proportion**: sizes in relation to one another.
>
> **Summative**: assessing the whole process after completion.

> **Exam tip**
>
> Make sure that you understand the importance of the design strategies outlined in this section as the exam may ask you to compare or discuss ways in which designers use these throughout the process.

> **Typical mistake**
>
> If you are not able to give real-life examples to justify your argument, your answer will lack depth.

Now test yourself

TESTED ☐

1 Describe three ways in which designers find inspiration to produce their design ideas. [3 marks]
2 Discuss the benefits of using the client throughout the design and manufacture process. [4 marks]
3 Explain how using a collaborative approach to design can be beneficial. [2 marks]

20 Communication of design ideas

There are many different techniques that can be used to communicate ideas and the designer's intent clearly to the client.

Freehand sketching

- Freehand sketching is done without the use of drawing aids.
- Ideas can be expressed quickly this way.
- Knowing the basics and practising them will build confidence.
- Using a mechanical pencil will allow for consistent line quality.
- Start with 2D freehand sketching to gain confidence. A starting point could be to take the five shapes shown and sketch them as 2D shapes.

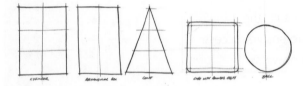

Figure 20.1 Freehand two-dimensional sketches of three-dimensional forms

- Sketches can be enhanced by adding thick and thin lines and colour **rendering** techniques.

Figure 20.2 Enhanced sketches

- Lightly sketching out the framework of a shape is a good starting point. This is called **crating** and the lines can then be added in bold.
- Adding a faint centre line to a drawing can add detail and also help with rendering.
- There is no set rule when it comes to adding darker or more weighted lines, but it is effective when added to **concave** curved edges.

> **Rendering**: adding colour to a drawing to enhance communication.
>
> **Crating**: a series of faint lines which help to build the final sketch.
>
> **Concave**: a surface that curves inwards.
>
> **Tone**: the deepness or brightness of a shade of colour.

Thick and thin lines

- The outline is a continuous and connected line that defines the outer boundary of an object. It is the boldest and thickest line of all.
- Use either a fine liner or outline pen to add this darker, thicker line to the outside edges of the design.

Rendering techniques

- Add colour, or texture, to enhance a sketch to better communicate design intent.
- Coloured pencils can be used to effectively add **tone** when rendering.
- Marker pens with layout paper also work well and allow a flat colour wash to be achieved.
- To sketch freehand in 3D, take a 2D idea or drawing and translate this into 3D.

2D and 3D drawings

REVISED

Isometric

- Isometric means 'equal measure'.
- 30° angles are applied to the sides of an object to give a 3D effect.
- This gives a more constructed way of showing an idea.
- Isometric grid paper makes it easier to draw in this style.
- Objects don't look realistic as there is no **perspective** applied to the drawing.

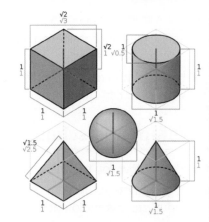

Figure 20.3 Isometric drawing

Perspective drawing

- Objects look more realistic as drawings tend to get smaller when they get closer to the vanishing lines drawn as a guide on the horizon line.
- One-point perspective drawing shows how things appear to get smaller as they get further away, **converging** towards a single 'vanishing point' on the horizon line.
- This is a popular drawing method for illustrators and architects to show objects from the front view or to look down something long, such as into a room.
- Two-point perspective drawing is a more realistic way to show 3D objects.
- Two vanishing points are used on the horizon line, one at either end.
- A vertical line is used to show the front corner of the object being drawn and other lines go to the vanishing points.
- Shadows: adding a shadow can make your 3D sketch look more realistic, as though your object is sitting on a surface, giving it weight.
- Linking boxes: these can be added to a design page to connect similar ideas together.
- Organic form: non-geometric shapes are more difficult to draw in 3D.
- Try to sketch out the idea in 2D form first showing different viewpoints.

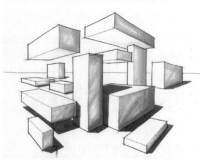

Figure 20.4 Two-point perspective drawing

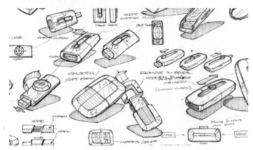

Figure 20.5 Sketch demonstrating use of shadows

Design ideas and sketches – a good way to start

- Designers use inspiration boards to generate ideas.
- Look at nature, mathematical patterns, existing products, your user's likes, architecture, the work of others and technological developments, to gain inspiration.
- From this, take shapes, colour, patterns and forms that inspire you. Make a cardboard window to focus into a part of an image and make it into a pattern.
- Images can be scanned into a software program to be **manipulated** further.

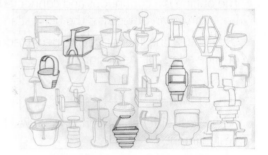

Figure 20.6 Thumbnail sketches

- Start the design section of your work with a sheet of thumbnail sketches to show a range of ideas.
- You don't need to filter out ideas that you don't like at this stage.
- Rendering isn't essential on thumbnail sketches but you could use a fine liner to highlight aspects of designs.
- 2D drawings are useful for this process as they are quicker to draw and put your thinking onto paper.
- Show evidence of how your research has influenced your designing.
- Refine ideas by considering materials and manufacture – begin to research these areas.
- Use all of your research findings to begin to develop ideas to a point where you can choose one or two to take further and develop.

> **Perspective**: the height, width and depth of an object drawn in relation to each other.
>
> **Converging**: meeting at a point.
>
> **Manipulated**: changed and controlled to fit the design.
>
> **Annotation**: text and comments added to a diagram to give explanation.

System and schematic diagrams

- These allow you to think logically about a problem and how to solve it.
- A good systems diagram shows where every process can be divided into input, process and output:
  - ○ Input: the problems and questions you are trying to solve.
  - ○ Process: the electrical and mechanical elements included in your design
  - ○ Output: what you think will be the end product.
- A schematic diagram uses symbols rather than realistic images. In fashion design, these diagrams are called 'flats' as no body is drawn.

Annotated drawings

- Remember to describe, explain and discuss your ideas in order to communicate them clearly.
- **Annotation** can help to clarify your design intention as sketches may not be able to show all of your ideas on paper.
- Describe: the shape and form of the design and whether it has any resemblance to other products, objects or architecture.
- Explain: giving explanations of materials, construction, scale and size, functionality and features.
- Discuss: what else do you need to state that the design drawing can't show? Can you give reasons for your decisions?

Exploded diagrams

- These are drawings which show the parts of a product separated out.
- Details such as construction, joining methods, strengthening methods or internal fittings can be shown.
- You can produce this type of drawing by tracing your 3D sketch, one part at a time, moving the original drawing so that the parts are not connected together.

Working drawings

- A **scale drawing** of your chosen idea can be used to construct and manufacture your idea.
- This can be drawn out by hand or using software packages. The drawing must be precise.
- They usually consist of a front, side and plan (top) view of the product.
- First- and third-angle orthographic drawings are the most common working drawings used.
- Dimensions are added to allow for manufacture (these are written above arrow lines, showing the measurements).

> **Scale drawing**: a drawing with accurate sizes that have been enlarged or reduced by a certain amount.

Figure 20.7 Exploded diagram

Audio and visual recordings

These can be added into your work to support your designing in the following ways:

- Interview a client for feedback.
- Explore a client's needs and problems first hand.
- You could explain your ideas more clearly verbally.
- Video a test model to look at comfort and ergonomics.
- Analyse and disassemble a product, explaining your findings.

Computer-based tools

- CAD can be used alongside a laser cutter to produce card models quickly and accurately.
- Virtual modelling: software allows for photorealistic 3D models to be produced and rendered.
- CAD helps to visualise the product when it is made. It can:
  - check sizes and proportions
  - test out different colour schemes and materials
  - place the product into context or a scene.

Modelling

- This allows you to appreciate your idea in 3D and can be tested out by your client.
- Details of the functionality and construction can be understood more clearly and problems solved.
- An idea or elements of different ideas that best solve the problem are modelled into a 3D form so that all views are understood.
- Modelling using card, styrofoam, MDF and modelling board are preferable as they are low cost and can be worked with quickly.
- Photographs of modelling and testing can be used to help with further development work.
- Evidence of development is crucial for your project as it demonstrates your ability to refine, evaluate and test an idea, along with continuing to research to solve problems.
- A product develops and becomes more accurate until it becomes a 'product prototype'. This allows for testing of manufacture, time, processes and assembly, which reduces mistakes and lowers costs in the long run.
- Foam modelling: styrofoam (blue and green foam) allows for 3D models to be made using hand tools, and finished using 'wet and dry' paper to give an accurate representation of the product.
- Foam-core board is lightweight and used for architectural models.
- Card modelling: corrugated card is normally used as it is available in different thicknesses and can be cut and joined easily.

Figure 20.8 Styrofoam model

> **Exam tip**
>
> Be able to identify the types of drawings highlighted in this chapter as you may be asked to redraw, complete or translate them in the exam.

> **Typical mistake**
>
> When asked to annotate in the exam, giving brief descriptions rather than explanations will cause you to miss out on the higher marks.

Now test yourself

1 What views are shown in an orthographic drawing? [3 marks]
2 Why are perspective drawings more useful than isometric? [1 mark]
3 List five common modelling materials and reasons they are useful. [5 marks]
4 Describe how CAD can be used to produce a prototype. [2 marks]

21 Prototype development

Producing prototypes or models is an essential part of the designing and making process. It allows testing to be carried out and client feedback to be collected to help refine a product further.

Designing and developing prototypes

- First models are basic to test out a concept.
- Client feedback is used to refine an idea and produce further models.
- Prototypes are usually made from cheaper materials although systems may be modelled with real components to allow for testing.
- Common materials used in modelling include: paper, card, MDF, polystyrene, foam board, plastics, clay, calico and breadboards.

Satisfying the requirements of the brief

- The client sets the design brief, which includes the required features.
- Prototyping helps the designer work out how to meet the brief.
- Small sections of the product can be modelled to check construction.

Responding to client wants and needs

- Commercial manufacture makes use of CAD and CAM to prototype ideas.
- To avoid expense and save time, CAD is used to develop products virtually to allow designers to see the design working.
- Clients can also test the product using these **virtual models** and suggest improvements.
- Prototypes are part of the manufacturing specification to show the manufacturer how the product will look and function.

Demonstrating innovation

- Physical prototypes can be used to see if the design appeals to the target market and is suitable for manufacture on a large scale.
- This tends to be for innovative products that are ahead of their time.
- Sometimes these innovations remain as prototypes and do not go into large-scale production.

Functionality

- Testing a product's performance is important to ensure that materials, money and time are used efficiently.
- Size and ergonomics can be tested using full-scale prototypes.
- In fashion, prototypes are used to check how the garment fits and drapes when worn.

> **Typical mistake**
>
> When asked in the exam to explain the benefits of using CAD and CAM to produce prototypes, you will miss out on marks if you give only superficial answers (such as they are 'quick').

Figure 21.1 Concept car used to test market appeal

> **Virtual model**: a model produced using CAD software to understand the product without actually making it.

Aesthetics

- Fashion and trends often determine the colours, shapes and patterns used.
- CAD allows designers to experiment with these elements quickly and easily.
- Fashion designers make use of this to show different colours and fabrics on a design.

Marketability

- Rapid prototyping allows a small number of products to be made economically.
- Rapid prototyping uses CNC machines to model quickly and in 3D.
- Complex shapes can be produced in this way.
- Prototypes made in this way can demonstrate how the product will look and function. The designer/manufacturer can understand how marketable the product will be.
- Feedback received can be used to improve the product and reactions from the target audience can be judged.

Figure 21.2 A cube being produced using a 3D printer

Evaluating prototypes

- A designer will test a prototype to ensure that the product is fit for its intended purpose.
- When you test your own models, it is important to get genuine client feedback.
- As a result of this feedback, modifications can be made and more models generated, to ensure that the end product is as suitable as it can be.
- In commercial manufacture, testing involves the client, members of the target market, experts in design and manufacture and experts in the use of the type of product.
- Focus groups are also used to gain the opinion of potential users.
- Prototypes are tested to ensure:
  o functionality
  o fitness for purpose
  o safety in use and manufacture
  o efficiency of manufacture.
- Final prototypes will be used to work out costings for materials and labour.

> **Exam tips**
>
> Be able to discuss the use of prototypes in both commercial (mass) production and one-off production.
>
> Be able to discuss specific examples of where prototypes have clearly been used effectively to develop a product further.

Now test yourself

TESTED

1 Describe how commercial manufacture makes use of CAD and CAM. [6 marks]
2 Explain the benefits of prototyping using 3D printers. [3 marks]
3 Explain why evaluating prototypes is an important part of the design and make process. [4 marks]
4 Why are prototypes tested? [3 marks]

22 Selection of materials and components

Functional qualities

REVISED ☐

- You need to prioritise the most important qualities that are needed in the product, such as absorbency, the ability to insulate or ease of care.
- The interaction between the fibres and the construction method used for the fabric will have a big impact on how the fabric performs. For example, cotton does not insulate well but if a cotton fabric is given a brushed finish it becomes warmer to wear.
- The choice of an appropriate fastening can add to the efficient functioning of the product – small decorative fastenings may look good but can be difficult to use; velcro can be opened and closed quickly but is bulky.

Cost

REVISED ☐

- Fabrics and components are available in different qualities and at prices to suit all budgets.
- Some are more expensive than others because of their fibre content, applied finishes or decorative techniques.
- Wider fabrics tend to cost more than narrower ones but may be more economical to use because pattern pieces can be placed side by side. Sometimes it is necessary to match patterns on the fabric or lay the pattern pieces so that they all face the same direction and this may mean that extra fabric needs to be bought to allow for this. The cost of components, including thread, needs to be considered when working out the cost of making a product.

> **Typical mistake**
>
> Many students state that products are made from fibres, for example cotton or polyester. Textile products are made from fabrics that are made from one or more fibres, and these fabrics can vary from ones that are very lightweight and floaty, to ones that are stiff and heavy. If you are asked to name or describe a fabric for a specific application, take care to describe the fabric type as well as the fibre content. For example, this could be a lightweight, plain, woven fabric made from polyester fibres, or a medium-weight, weft-knitted, jersey fabric from cotton fibres.

Availability

REVISED ☐

- Fabrics and components are available in a very wide range of colours, patterns and weights, although fabrics are made in a limited number of standard widths.
- A wide range of components are made in basic and fashion colours to work with the fabrics available.

Figure 22.1 Many different fabrics are available at different prices

23 Tolerances

Tolerances

- Very fine tolerances are difficult to achieve when working with textile materials as they have a lot of give in them when compared to materials such as timber and metal.
- Some textile techniques and parts of the product need to be manufactured to a small tolerance or they will not fit together accurately and that would spoil the appearance. For example:
  - individual shapes to make an appliqué design must be cut accurately or they will not fit together
  - a pocket must be sewn in the correct place on the front of a shirt or it will not be pleasing to look at.

You can read more about tolerances in textile-based materials in Chapter 11.

24 Material management

Cutting efficiently and minimising waste

Wasting textile materials can have cost and environmental implications, so it is important to use fabric as economically as possible. When planning fabric layouts:

- Follow the layout given if using a **commercial pattern** and check that all pieces for the style you are making have been included.
- If using a pattern that you have made yourself, make sure that you have included seam and hem allowances on all pieces or the product will be too small when sewn together.
- Consider the width of the fabric as pieces can often be laid side by side on wide fabric, but may need to be laid end to end on narrower widths.
- It may be possible to dovetail some of the pattern pieces to avoid wasting fabric.
- If the fabric has a **one-way pattern** or **nap**, all the pattern pieces will need to face the same way – this may mean that fabric cannot be used as economically as when the pattern pieces can be dovetailed.
- If the fabric is checked or has a prominent pattern, you will need to plan the layout carefully so that patterns are matched across seams and the pattern is placed to give the best effect on the product – this will probably require extra fabric.
- It is very important that the straight grain line on the pattern is placed parallel to the fabric selvedge, or the fabric will not hang correctly in the finished product.
- Plan the layout on a large table with the fabric width marked out – you can use metre rulers to do this.
- Move the pattern pieces around to find the most economical position and calculate the amount of fabric needed, rounding up to the nearest 10 cm.

Figure 24.1 Fabrics with a one-way design must be cut so that the pattern pieces all face the same way

> **Commercial pattern**: ready-made pattern templates used to make textile products.
>
> **One-way pattern**: a design on the fabric that has one direction.
>
> **Nap**: a one-directional raised or brushed surface.

Using appropriate marking-out methods, data points and co-ordinates

- Seam and hem allowances can be marked onto the fabric before cutting using tailor's chalk or a special fabric pen or pencil. The width of the seam allowance is usually 15 mm, the width of a tape measure.
- Pattern markings can be transferred to the fabric after cutting using tailor's tacks or a tracing wheel and tracing paper.
- The **fabric selvedge** is a critical **datum point** when cutting fabric.
- The straight grain line on the pattern template must always be parallel to the selvedge or the fabric will not hang correctly and patterns such as stripes and checks will not appear 'straight' on the finished product. If the fabric is folded so that the pattern can be cut out of double fabric, check that the selvedges are exactly on top of each other, otherwise the grain will not be straight on both layers.

- When measuring the distance between the straight grain line and the selvedge, a tape measure must be used. It may help to pin in place one end of the grain line marked on the pattern, to stop it moving while the other end is checked and nudged into place, so that it is the same distance from the selvedge.
- The centre line of a checked fabric is also a datum line. Make sure that it is laid on the centre lines of the product so that the pattern is balanced on the finished product.

> **Fabric selvedge:** the finished edge of the fabric where the weft turns around the warp during weaving to leave an edge that does not fray.
>
> **Datum point:** a known point of reference from which further measurements can be made.

Figure 24.2 The centre line of a checked fabric is a useful datum line and should be placed along the centre line of the product to give a pleasing and balanced effect

Exam practice answers at **www.hoddereducation.co.uk/6 myrevisionnotesdownloads**

25 Specialist tools and equipment

There are many specialist tools used for sewing, cutting and pressing fabric, and they must be used safely and efficiently to make products of the highest quality.

Equipment for sewing

- Sewing machines all thread up and work in the same basic way. There are three main types:
  1 Basic machines that do straight and zig-zag stitching can make buttonholes and some basic decorative stitches.
  2 Automatic sewing machines can sew functional and decorative stitches that are pre-programmed into the machine.
  3 Computerised sewing machines have a wide range of pre-programmed stitches and can also stitch motifs that have been designed on a computer or scanned into the machine from a website.

- Sewing machines have interchangeable feet to make some sewing tasks easier and more efficient, such as a zip foot, buttonhole foot or walking foot. It is important to read the manual that comes with the machine in order to use it safely and make best use of its features.

Figure 25.1 **Using two needles, an overlocker can sew and neaten the seam in one operation**

- Overlockers are a specialised type of sewing machine that only has bobbins of thread on the top of the machine and has one or two needles. Using one needle, they are used to neaten seams by trimming the edge of the fabric and covering the cut edge with stitches at the same time. They are used extensively in commercial manufacture, as by using two needles they can sew and neaten the seam at the same time.

Ironing and pressing equipment

- Irons have thermostats that can be set to temperatures between 60°C and 200°C according to the fabric used. They are used to press work during manufacture and when applying iron-on interfacing. Steam irons are the most useful.

Cutting tools

Textile processes involve a lot of cutting and there are many different tools available to make these processes more efficient. These include: shears, rotary cutters, pinking shears, embroidery scissors, unpickers, snippers and craft knives.

Measuring tools

REVISED

Making good quality products involves accurate measuring.

A tape measure is a flexible plastic tape useful for taking body measurements and checking that the straight grain line is parallel to the selvedge when laying patterns on fabric. It is worth remembering that tape measures are 15 mm wide – the same measurement as the seam allowance on most pattern templates.

Pins and needles

REVISED

Different types of pins and needles are used for different fabrics and tasks.

- **Pins** are made of steel or nickel-plated steel and may have plastic or glass heads. Pins should always be sharp or they will snag fabrics.
- **Hand-sewing needles** come in different sizes from 1–12 – the higher the number, the finer the needle. They include the following:
  - Sharps are long sharp needles used for general sewing.
  - Crewels have a sharp point and a long eye and are used for embroidery.
  - Betweens are short sharp needles used for fine sewing.
  - Bodkins have a blunt point and a long eye and are used for threading elastic and cords through casings.
  - Ball point needles have a rounded point that can pass through knitted fabrics more easily than sharp pointed needles.
- **Machine-sewing needles** come in a range of sizes – the higher the number, the thicker the needle. They include the following:
  - General purpose needles in sizes 60–100 are used for most machine sewing.
  - Ball point needles have rounded points for sewing knitted fabrics.
  - Denim needles have an extra-sharp tip and are used for sewing tough fabrics.
  - Leather needles have a wedge-shaped tip and are used for sewing leather without tearing it.
  - Twin and triple needles are joined together in a row and used for decorative stitching.

26 Specialist techniques and processes

Specialist techniques and processes

Accuracy can be achieved by:

- making sure that the straight grain line on the pattern template is exactly parallel to the fabric selvedge
- choosing the most appropriate construction technique that gives a strong and neat finish and appearance to the product, for example seams and edge finishes.
- ironing fabric flat and removing creases before cutting out and pressing work as you go along at each stage of manufacture. This ensures that work is flat and ready for the next stage of manufacture.
- using interfacing to give strength and shape to certain parts of the product. The weight and colour needs to be chosen carefully so it does not spoil the hang and appearance of the final product.
- checking that the sewing machine is threaded correctly and that the settings are right for your fabric before you start stitching your product.

27 Surface treatments and finishes

Surface treatments and finishes

Many different decorative techniques can be used to enhance a textile product.

- Fabric printing may be done using screen printing or dye sublimation.
- Care must be taken to make sure that the print is the correct size and placed accurately on the product, and that the colour is even and not smudged.
- Special care needs to be taken when a print motif is repeated, as small mistakes can quickly become large errors along the length or width of a fabric.
- Embroidery can be done on a computerised sewing or embroidery machine or by hand, which will give less accurate results.

Figure 27.1 Each repeat of a printed pattern must be accurate to ensure a high-quality product

Exam tip

You may be asked to describe how to work a construction or decorative technique. It may help you to use labelled diagrams to explain a process with which you are familiar. Check your description to make sure that another person could follow your instructions and get the right result.

Now test yourself

1 What special care needs to be taken when laying pattern pieces on fabric with a nap? [1 mark]
2 Explain three functional qualities that will be needed in fabric to be used for casual trousers. [3 marks]
3 Give two problems in a finished textile product that might be caused by not placing the grain line on the pattern parallel to the selvedge of the fabric. [2 marks]
4 Why is it important to press work after each process has been completed? [1 mark]
5 What type of needle is best for sewing knitted fabric? [1 mark]

Exam practice

1 State two ways that cultural factors can have an influence on the design of textile products. [2 marks]

2 State two places where a part of a textile product must be manufactured to a fine tolerance. [2 marks]

3 Explain the importance of the fabric grain line in ensuring that a textile product is made to a high quality. [3 marks]

4 Name a manufacturing system that would be used to make fashion tops to be sold in a high street chain store during the summer season. Explain why the system would be the most appropriate. [3 marks]

5 Name the most appropriate type of:
   a) sewing machine needle for sewing knitted fabrics
   b) hand-sewing needle for threading elastic through a casing. [2 marks]

6 Garments need to be shaped so that they fit the human body. Name and describe one method of giving shape to a product. [5 marks]

7 State three points to be considered when deciding on the type of seam to use when making a textile product. [3 marks]

8 Explain how using templates/patterns and jigs increases accuracy in production. [3 marks]

ONLINE

Success in the examination

You will take one written paper that is worth 50 per cent of your total marks. The paper is divided into three sections:

- Section A: Core technical principles (20 marks)
- Section B: Specialist technical principles (30 marks)
- Section C: Designing and making principles (50 marks)

When will the exam be completed?

REVISED

There is one opportunity to take the exam – in the summer term of your final year.

How long will I have to complete the exam?

REVISED

- The exam is two hours long and each question has a guide time to help you complete the paper.
- You should practise working past papers and sample questions within the allotted time.

What type of questions will appear in the exam paper?

REVISED

Section A consists of 20 multiple-choice questions that test your knowledge of the core technical principles.

Here is a typical Section A multiple-choice question.

Example

1 Which of the following is a composite material:
   a) Iron
   b) Teak
   c) Kevlar
   d) Cartridge paper

The correct answer is c) Kevlar and for one mark you should indicate it as:

Example

1 Which of the following is a composite material:
   a) Iron
   b) Teak
   c) Kevlar
   d) Cartridge paper

Don't answer a multiple-choice question like this:

> **Exam tip**
>
> Never leave a multiple-choice question blank. See if you can eliminate some of the answers you believe to be definitely wrong and then make an educated guess from among the remaining options.

If you mark any more than one box, your answer will not be awarded a mark even if one of your answers is correct.

Section B consists of a mixture of short answer and long answer questions. This section will test your knowledge of specialist technical principles.

This is a typical Section B question:

> **Example**
>
> 1 Many products are given a finish to enhance their appearance and give protection. For a material of your choice, name a suitable finish and explain how this finish would be applied.   **[4 marks]**

Section C consists of a number of short and long answer questions. This section will test your knowledge of design and making principles.

This is a typical Section C question:

> **Example**
>
> **Baby's high chair**
>
> 3 Study the picture of the baby's high chair. Discuss the suitability of the product in terms of its:
>   ○ suitability for the user
>   ○ aesthetics
>   ○ environmental impact.

Tips on preparing for the exam

REVISED ☐

- If you did not understand a topic when it was covered in class, you are unlikely to understand it when revising. Make sure you ask at the end of a lesson if you're unsure of any of the material covered.
- Being absent from school can leave a big hole in your knowledge. Make sure that you catch up any missed work.
- Don't leave revision till the end of the course. Test yourself at the end of each topic.
- Use past papers, online materials and revision guides to help you practise exam-type questions.
- Plan your revision time in the weeks leading up to the exam.
- Make revision cards to help you compartmentalise your understanding.
- Work with other students to test each other.

Approaching the paper

- Make sure you know the date, time and location of your exam.
- Get a good night's sleep. Make sure you have eaten and that you are hydrated.
- Arrive early and make sure you have all your equipment with you.
- Read the instructions on the front cover of the question paper. This will tell you what you have to do.
- Read each question carefully at least twice. This will help you to understand exactly what information you need to give.
- The question will tell you how many marks are available for this question. Use this to gauge how much detail you need to put into your answer.
- The question will tell you how long you should take to answer the question. Use this to help you pace yourself during the exam.
- If you finish early, go back and reread the questions and your answers. You will usually find that you have remembered more detail. You may also be able to spot any mistakes that you may have made.

Sample examination questions

Section A

Section B

In the exam you will be able to answer Section B questions in relation to **one** chosen material category or system. The sample questions included here each focus on a different material category or system.

Sample question: Textile-based materials

Example

Explain how the sourcing, processing and disposal of textile materials can impact on the environment.
Give examples in your answer. [9 marks]

Candidate response

Cotton is a natural fibre but is not good for the environment because it needs to have lots of chemical pesticides and fertilisers sprayed on to the crops to make them grow. The chemicals can poison the ground and any rivers and lakes nearby. This means that other crops may not grow and fish will be poisoned. Cotton is a very thirsty plant and needs a lot of water, which can cause rivers and lakes to dry up. The Aral Sea disaster was caused when farmers diverted the water for their cotton crops. The water may be needed by people who do not have enough water to drink. Organic cotton is better for the environment as it is grown without chemicals.

Polyester comes from oil that is non-renewable and supplies are running out, but it can be made from recycled plastic bottles. Polyester takes many years to break down when it is sent to landfill.

When fibres are turned into yarns and fabrics, a lot of energy is needed to power the machines' work and this also has a bad effect on the environment.

Dyeing fabrics uses a lot of chemicals and water and if these are not disposed of properly this can pollute the land and rivers. Applying finishes such as flame retardant and stain repellent can mean that the chemicals used pollute land. Even when textiles are sent to landfill, the dyes and chemicals can still pollute the land.

When textile products wear out or people do not want them anymore they are often sent to landfill and this is a problem because we are running out of space for landfill sites. Reusing the textile materials to make new products is better, or giving them to charity shops means that other people can use them if they are not worn out.

Mark scheme

The assessment for a 9-mark question like this would usually use performance descriptors like those shown below:

Band	Descriptor
7–9 marks	Several points relating to different ways in which textiles impact on the environment with explanation of the issues. A range of appropriate examples is given to illustrate the issues.
4–6 marks	Some points relating to the ways in which textiles impact on the environment with some explanation of the issues. More than one appropriate example is given to illustrate the issues.
1–3 marks	A limited number of simple or obvious ways that textiles impact on the environment with little explanation of the issues. An example has been given which may not be fully explained.
0 marks	No response

Section C

Example

Explain how the following are used when designing a product.
- Focus groups
- Ergonomics
- Anthropometric data   [3 x 3 marks]

Candidate response 1

- Focus groups:

Large companies use these to test out their ideas as it involves a group of people giving their opinion through a discussion. This feedback allows for useful primary research to be collected at the initial investigation stages of the design process. It also helps a designer make useful modifications as prototypes can be tested with the focus group too.

- Ergonomics:

Ergonomics is the consideration of how a person interacts with a product. A designer would need to consider this to ensure that the product they design is comfortable and easy to use. Considering aspects such as size, shape, weight and colour make the product more efficient to use.

● Anthropometrics:

Anthropometrics is the size of humans, for example their height, hand span or leg length. This data is used by a designer to ensure that the product they design fits the intended audience. It is common for the 5th to 95th percentile of data to be used, ignoring the extreme sizes. Using anthropometrics ensures that the product is ergonomically designed.

Candidate response 2

● Focus groups:

A type of research where lots of people try out a product

● Ergonomics:

How easy a product is to use

● Anthropometrics:

The size of humans

Mark scheme

For a 3-mark answer the following style of assessment might be used.

Band	Descriptor
3	Three points well made or two points made and justified or two points made and an example given.
2	Two simple points made or a point made and justified or exemplified.
1	A simple point made
0	Nothing worthy of credit

Assessment comment

Candidate One would score 3 marks each time as they give a full explanation of each term and link it back to how a designer might use it to design a product. Detailed statements showing a good understanding.

Candidate Two would score 1 mark for their answers to both ergonomics and anthropometrics as they recall only a simple statement which is a definition of the term. Their answer for focus group may score 2 marks as there is slightly more to their response.

Glossary

Absorbency: how well a material draws up water.

Aesthetics: the style and appearance of a material.

Alignment: when something is in line with something else.

Alloy: a mixture of two or more metals designed to improve the quality of the metal for a given purpose.

Annotation: text and comments added to a diagram to give explanation.

Anodising: a protective oxide layer applied to the surface of aluminium.

Anthropometrics: human dimensions.

Assembly-line production: a series of workers and machines in a factory who progressively assemble identical items.

Automated: a system run completely by machinery through computer control.

Automation: the use of automatic equipment in manufacturing.

Basic blocks: a pattern for each part of a garment that will make a basic garment shape when sewn together.

Batch production: production in which a limited number of the same product is made during a particular period of time.

Bauxite: ore containing aluminium.

Bell-crank linkage: a linkage that changes the direction of the input motion through 90°.

Bespoke: a product that has been specifically made for a client to fulfil their needs.

Biodegradable: something which breaks down and degrades naturally.

Biomimicry: the design of products modelled on nature.

Biopolymers: polymers which are made from plant material such as corn starch.

Blended fabrics: fabrics containing two or more different fibres.

Calendars: rollers which are used in the manufacture of paper to flaten and thin the material.

Cam and follower: a mechanism that converts rotary motion into reciprocating motion when the cam rotates and the follower moves up and down.

Carded: combing staple fibres so that they all lie parallel to each other ready for spinning into a yarn.

Casting: a method of heating metal into a molten state and pouring it into a pre-prepared mould.

Cellulose: fibres which are naturally occurring in plant material.

CNC: computer numerically controlled.

Commercial pattern: ready-made pattern templates used to make textile products.

Composite material: a material that combines the properties of two or more materials.

Computer-aided design (CAD): design work created on computer software packages which can control CAM machines.

Computer-aided manufacture (CAM): manufacture of products using machines which are controlled by computers.

Computer numerically controlled (CNC): automated machines which are operated by computers.

Concave: a surface that curves inwards.

Conductive fabrics: textiles that conduct electricity.

Contamination: exposure to a polluting substance.

Contemporary: present-day design.

Converging: meeting at a point.

Conversion: (of timber) the process of cutting a log up into planks.

Co-operative: a business owned, governed and self-managed by its workers.

Crating: a series of faint lines which help to build the final sketch.

Crease: make a shallow indent in the material so that it can be folded easily.

Cross filing: a method of shaping metal using files.

Crowdfunding: a method of funding a project by raising money from large numbers of people using the internet.

Cubist: early 20th-century design, making use of geometry and interlocking planes.

Culture: the values, beliefs, customs and behaviours of groups of people and societies.

Datum point: a known starting point; a point of reference from which further measurements can be made.

Depth-stop: a mechanical means of setting the depth that a drill bit will cut, used for quality control.

Die cutter: shapes can be punched or stamped out cleanly.

Draw filing: a method of smoothing the edges of metal.

Dyeing: the permanent application of colour to a fibre or fabric to give a uniform colour.

Effort: an input force applied to move an object.

Electrical insulator: something which does not conduct electricity.

Engrave: carve or etch onto the surface of an object.

Ergonomics: human interaction with products.

E-textiles: textiles that use smart materials.

Ethics: moral principles.

Evolve: to develop gradually.

Exploitation: the action or fact of treating someone unfairly in order to benefit from their work.

Extrusion: an industrial process involving heating polymer granules and forcing them through a die to produce long, uniform, cross-sectional polymer products.

Fabric selvedge: the finished edge of the fabric where the weft turns around the warp during weaving to leave an edge that does not fray.

Face side and face edge: two adjacent surfaces of wood that have been planed flat and square.

Fair trade: a movement that aims to achieve fair and better trading conditions and opportunities that promote sustainability for developing countries.

Felling: the process of cutting down trees.

Ferrous metals: metals that contain iron, are magnetic but are prone to rusting.

Finite resource: a resource that will run out.

First-order lever: a lever that has the fulcrum anywhere between the effort and the load.

Fission: division or splitting of an atom.

Flexible manufacturing system (FMS): flexibility in a system which allows it to react to predicted or unpredicted changes during manufacturing.

Flow soldering: an industrial method of soldering where a solder paste is melted by heating a PCB.

Focus group: a large group of people who feed back their opinions.

Forest Stewardship Council (FSC): an organisation which helps to manage trees and avoid deforestation.

Fossil fuels: coal, oil and gas which are finite resources and are found naturally.

Fractional distillation: the process of separating crude oil into its different parts.

Friction: the resistance to movement when two surfaces rub together.

Functional: an object which works well and fulfils its purpose or job.

Functionality: how well an object or a material will fit its intended purpose.

Galvanising: a protective coating of zinc applied to the surface of steel.

Gear train: a mechanism with two wheels with teeth around the edge that interlock and transmit rotary motion and torque; a line of meshing gears.

Generator: a machine for converting mechanical energy into electricity.

Geometric: use of shapes and angles in design.

Global warming: an increase in the temperature of the Earth's atmosphere due to higher levels of CO_2.

Go-no-go gauge: a special tool that checks the size of a metal component.

Greenhouse effect: the effect of pollution in the atmosphere causing the sun's heat to get trapped in the lower atmosphere and warm up the planet.

Green timber: timber that has just been felled and contains a lot of moisture.

Haematite: ore containing iron.

Hardwoods: woods which come from deciduous trees and are generally hard and durable.

Human factors: issues relating to people.

Iconic: product which is held in high regard, is well known, has influenced others or withstood the test of time.

Ingeo™: a high-performance biodegradable fibre made from corn starch.

Ingots: bars of metal that can be processed.

Injection moulding: an industrial process where polymer granules are heated and injected into a mould.

Innovation: inventing and developing ideas into products.

Innovative: advanced or original.

Input device: an electrical or mechanical sensor that uses signals from the environment and converts them into signals that can be passed to processing devices and components.

Integrated circuit (IC): a self-contained circuit made up of separate components that act as process devices in an electronic system; a miniature electronic circuit on a semi-conductor.

Interfacing: a woven or non-woven fabric used as an extra layer to give additional strength and help to keep the shape of a textile product.

Intricate: design which is complex.

Jig: a three-dimensional aid to a production process.

Just in time (JIT) production: an approach to production which reduces flow time as items needed are delivered just in time for the assembly of the product.

KD (knock-down) fittings: commercially-made fittings generally used with self-assembly furniture.

Lean manufacturing: focusing on reduction of waste when manufacturing.

Lever: a simple mechanism that changes an input motion and force into an output motion and force.

Life cycle assessment: understanding the impact a product has, from the extraction of its raw materials to its disposal at the end of its useful lifespan.

Light-dependent resistor (LDR): an input device used to detect light levels, in which resistance increases in low light and decreases in intense light.

Light-emitting diode (LED): an output device that produces light.

Linear motion: movement in a straight line.

Linkage: a mechanism that transfers force and changes the direction of movement.

Load: an output force.

Manipulated: changed and controlled to fit the design.

Manufactured boards: man-made boards that come in large sizes and are usually flat and stable.

Market pull: where users want an existing product to be improved or redeveloped to meet their needs.

Mass production: manufacturing in large quantities over a long period of time.

Mechanism: a device that changes an input motion into an output motion.

Microcontroller: a small computer with a single integrated circuit used to provide functionality and control.

Microencapsulated: Fibres with nano-sized chemical capsules in the fibre structure. Rubbing activates the capsules which release their contents.

Microfibres: very fine fibres – 60 times finer than human hair – made from polyamide or polyester.

Milling: the machining of material to produce grooves, slots and flat surfaces.

Modern material: a material that has recently been developed.

Monomers: the individual building blocks used to create polymers.

Nap: a one-directional raised or brushed surface.

Natural fibres: fibres from plant and animal sources.

Nested: also known as tessellated; fitting as many shapes as possible next to one another on a sheet of material, with minimal space in between, in order to avoid waste.

Non-ferrous metals: metals that do not contain iron and therefore do not rust.

Non-finite resource: a resource that if managed properly will not run out.

Non-woven fabrics: fabrics made directly from fibres without the need to make them into yarns first.

Obsolete: something which is no longer useful or which is out of date.

One-off manufacture: manufacture in which only one complete product is made.

One-way pattern: a fabric design that has one direction.

Opacity: the density of a material and whether light can be seen through it.

Ore: rock which contains metal.

Organic cotton: cotton grown with fewer chemical pesticides and fertilisers than standard cotton.

Orthographic: a 2D working drawing which shows the views and dimensions of a product so that a third party can manufacture it.

Ornate: highly decorative.

Oscillating motion: movement swinging from side to side.

Output device: a device that sends out information to the environment.

Patent: a form of intellectual property which protects a designer's ideas.

Patterns: a marking-out aid which ensures exact copies of a shape or part can be made.

Perforate: to make a series of cuts in a form of a dotted line.

Perspective: the height, width and depth of an object drawn in relation to each other.

Photochromic: a material that reacts to light.

Pick and place machine: an industrial machine used to surface mount electronic components onto the surface of a PCB.

Pigments: materials added to a polymer to change its colour.

Pivot or fulcrum: a fixed point around which a mechanism moves.

Planed all round (PAR): timber that has all sides planed; also known as 'planed square edge (PSE)'.

Planed both sides (PBS): timber that has had two sides planed.

Planed square edge (PSE): timber that has all sides planed; also know as 'planed all round (PAR)'.

Plying: twisting two or more single yarns together to make a multi-ply yarn.

Polymerisation: joining monomers together to form polymers.

Pop art: art based on modern popular culture.

Postmodernistic: designs which consider the aesthetics of an object more than its functionality.

Potatopak: packaging material made from starch.

Precious metal: a rare metal that is expensive, such as gold.

Press forming: the process of softening a thermoforming polymer and pressing it into a mould.

Primary research: investigations carried out first hand.

Printed circuit board (PCB): a board that supports and connects electronic components.

Process device: a device that handles information received from an input device and turn outputs on and/or off.

Profit margin: financial gain between what has been spent and what has been earned.

Programmable interface controller (PIC): a programmable integrated circuit.

Proportion: sizes in relation to one another.

Prototype: a first or initial version of a product; an early sample, model, or release of a product, made to test a concept or a process.

Pulleys and belts: a mechanism of two small wheels connected by a belt that transmit rotary motion.

Push/pull or parallel-motion linkage: a linkage in which the direction of motion and the magnitude of the forces are the same.

Quality control: checks made during manufacture to ensure accuracy is maintained.

Raw material: material before it has undergone processing; the state a material is first found in (for example, ores from the ground before they are processed into metals).

Recessed: set back into the surface.

Reciprocating motion: movement backwards and forwards in a straight line.

Recycled: material which has had another use or purpose previously and has been reprocessed and made into a new product.

Refining: the processing of crude oil.

Regenerated fibres: fibres made by chemically modifying cellulose from spruce trees or cotton linters.

Rendering: adding colour to a drawing to enhance communication.

Renewable: a source of material or energy which, if managed responsibly, will not run out.

Robotics: technology involved in the design, building, operation and use of robots.

Rotary motion: movement round in a circle.

Rough sawn: timber straight from the saw.

Scale drawing: a drawing with accurate relative sizes that have been enlarged or reduced by a certain amount.

Scoring: lightly cutting the surface of a material so that it folds cleanly.

Seasoning: the process of removing moisture from newly-converted planks.

Secondary research: using the investigations of others.

Second-order lever: a lever that has the load and effort on the same side of the fulcrum.

Semi-precious metal: metal such as copper, that is more expensive than common metals such as steel.

Serrated: a blade that has ridges in it to allow it to perforate a material.

Shape memory alloy (SMA): a metal that will return to its original shape when placed in hot water.

Smart material: a material that reacts to environmental changes such as heat and light.

Smelting: the process of extracting metal from ore.

Softwoods: woods which come from coniferous trees that are relatively fast growing.

Spinning: twisting fibres together to make a yarn.

Stabilisers: materials added to a polymer to improve its resistance to UV light.

Standard components: mass produced parts that are all identical and can be used and replaced in many products easily.

Standardised: in which all parts are the same and identical so can be replaced easily.

Standardised sizes: a set of body measurements that conform to the British Standards Institute (BSI) standard sizing.

Stock size: standard form of materials for purchase and manufacture.

Sub-assembly: a separate manufacturing line that makes small sections of a product, such as collars, ready to add to the final product being made.

Summative: assessing the whole process after completion.

Sustainability: design which considers environmental impacts, both in the long and short term; designing to maintain the environment today and in the future.

Switch: an input device that senses when pressure is applied.

Synthetic fibres: fibres manufactured from oil-based chemicals.

System: a set of parts or components that work together and provide functionality to products and processes.

Tanilising: a method of pressure-treating wood with a preservative.

Task analysis: looking at the design task or brief in depth and asking questions.

Technical textiles: textiles manufactured for their functional capabilities.

Technology push: where new technologies or materials are developed and designers develop new products that use them.

Template: a pattern shape, usually made from paper or card, used to cut out fabric to the size and shape required; a two-dimensional profile of an object that is to be cut.

Tessellation: the arranging of shapes to minimise waste.

Thermal insulator: material which does not conduct heat.

Thermistor: an input device in which resistance changes with changes in temperature.

Thermochromatic: a material that reacts to heat.

Thermoforming polymers: polymers that can be formed and shaped with the use of heat.

Thermoplastic fibres: these soften when heated and can be heat-set into new shapes.

Thermosetting polymers: polymers that once formed cannot be reformed with the use of heat.

Third-order lever: a lever that has the load and effort on the same side of the fulcrum, but the load is further away from the fulcrum and therefore the effort needed is greater than the load.

Tolerance: the acceptable difference between the upper and lower given sizes; the allowable amount of variation of a specified dimension within which quality will still be assured.

Tolerance level: the acceptable variation in the size a product or part of a product, usually given as an upper and a lower limit.

Tone: the deepness or brightness of a shade of colour.

Torque: a turning force that causes rotation.

Triangulation: use of triangles in structures to increase strength.

Turbine: a wheel inside a machine which is rotated by a flow of water or other fluid, or steam or gas.

Turning: a method of producing cylinders and cones using a centre lathe.

Vacuum forming: a process that involves heating a thermoforming polymer and sucking it around a mould.

Virtual marketing: marketing techniques that get websites, social networks or their users to pass on marketing messages to other websites and users to increase brand awareness.

Virtual model: a model produced using CAD software to understand the product without actually making it.

Virtual retailing: selling products on the internet.